# INTRODUCTION TO PHYSICS AND ENGINEERING

## A Home-Based Workbook

# INTRODUCTION TO PHYSICS AND ENGINEERING

A Home-Based Workbook

Dale W. Cox

AN **EDIBLE KNOWLEDGE®** SERIES WORKBOOK

ISBN: 978-1-948515-07-8
Ebook ISBN: 978-1-948515-08-5

Library of Congress Cataloging-in-Publication Data is available.

Published by Beakers & Bricks, LLC

Cover design by Glen M. Edelstein
Interior design by Glen M. Edelstein and David Dalley

Photographs by Dale W. Cox, unless otherwise specified in Pictures and Illustrations Attributions

Edible Knowledge® logo art by LeAnne Cox and Glen Edelstein
Edible Knowledge® is a registered trademark of Beakers & Bricks, LLC
Printed in the United States of America

Beakers & Bricks, LLC
PO Box 1014
Asheboro, North Carolina 27204
www.beakersandbricks.com

Special thanks to Dr. Lynn Ogden for his help reviewing the manuscript.

Disclaimer/caution: The food science experiment at the end of this workbook involves high temperatures and a sharp knife. Please take every precaution to avoid injury.

# CONTENTS

# PREFACE AND INTRODUCTION

**Hello, fellow science, physics, engineering, and LEGO® enthusiasts!** And a very special welcome to those who may be completing this workbook to fill a science credit. I'm a professional food scientist and worked in the industry for twenty-three years for companies such as Kellogg's®, Kraft®, Post Consumer Brands®, and Gorton's® Seafood, developing food products you see in the store. The Edible Knowledge® brand, designed by my company, Beakers & Bricks, is publishing a series of *Introduction to Food Science* workbooks that teach many food science principles related to the main components of food (water, carbohydrates, protein, fat) and provide hands-on experiments, some of which you get to eat! I love food science! You can make a great living at it, and it's also interesting because you see it around you every day—in the kitchen while making dinner and in the prepared foods you purchase and consume.

While I love food science, one of my first real passions was for LEGO® bricks, especially the LEGO® Technic™ elements.

A LEGO® Technic™ brick set[1]

These sets have elements that include universal joints, axles, gears, and other components that mimic hydraulics. You can make remote-controlled models that move and behave much like the real machines they emulate. Building with these pieces is fun, the possibilities are endless, and they lend themselves nicely to experimenting with and learning about scientific physics principles. Many books and programs on the market that teach science use LEGO® bricks. However, I've found them lacking in substance.

I heard a comment similar to mine at a homeschool conference when a parent said that much of the fun science curriculum available is "a mile wide and an inch deep," meaning they cover a lot of material without getting into any depth. I find this frustrating and it's one reason the Edible Knowledge series came about. In these workbooks, topics are presented in an engaging and in-depth fashion. Further, the questions aren't designed to require regurgitations of what's in the chapter—they require application and thought. Rarely is there one correct answer, as is the case for most everything in life.

In the same fashion, in *Introduction to Physics and Engineering,* I have combined my passion for LEGO® bricks with my love of science and endeavor to teach the principles in as much depth as possible. The goal is for students to see what they're learning around them, understand practical application of the principles, and develop inquisitive minds. This book follows the Edible Knowledge series model, with a *What Do You*

*Think?* section at the end of each chapter, including a *Journaling Idea* and a *Chapter Review*. I hope you find this different and enjoyable.

Note: the instructions for building the models aren't like what you are used to in sets you purchase. I used photographs instead of step-by-step directions, and each picture incorporates multiple steps. You need to use a sharp eye to determine what to do next. It can be challenging, but you can do it! If you still can't figure it out, call or email. We'll get you straightened out. A full list of parts and pieces needed and how to get them is at the end of this section.

Of course, since this workbook is in the Edible Knowledge series, an interesting food science experiment is included!

I hope you enjoy learning about physics and engineering using these fun LEGO® elements. And have a blast with the food science experiment! If you do, look up my other food science workbooks. There's a LOT more where this came from!

Dale W. Cox, ©2019
Food Scientist
LEGO® Enthusiast

Note: The models in this workbook were developed with the goal of keeping the total number of parts, and therefore cost, down. With additional pieces, more aesthetically pleasing models can be built. I encourage you to experiment and modify your models. I'd love to see your new creations, so please send pictures!

## PARTS, PIECES, AND TERMINOLOGY

First, a little on LEGO® brick terminology. Regular bricks are referred to by the number of studs—the raised parts on top. They can be any number of studs wide and any number in length. For example, below is pictured a 2x4 brick (read "two by four"), one of the most basic pieces.

This piece is two studs wide by four studs long. Here's a 1x2 brick with a hole in the middle:

Axles are indicated by how many studs long they are. Line up the axle next to a brick and count the number of studs. The axle's lengths in each experiments' parts list are marked by a red number. The example below picture shows axles that are six and eight studs long.

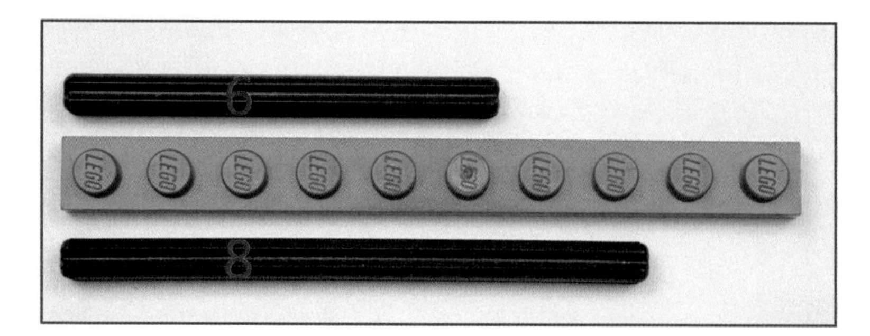


Other bricks are more unique in shape and size, and most are available in more than one color. A specific design of a brick has a **Design Number.** The same brick design is interchangeable with other bricks of the same design, even if they are a different color. To specify both a color and design, you need the **Item Number.** For example, a 1x2 brick with a hole in it has a certain **Design Number,** but that part can be red, blue, or many other colors. The red and blue versions each have a unique **Item Number,** which specifies both the design and color.

| | Design Number | Item Number |
|---|---|---|
| | 3700 | 3700021 |
| | 3700 | 3700023 |

With that understanding, below are the LEGO® parts and pieces needed for the experiments in this workbook. You may already have many of them in your collection. For those missing, they're listed in the table by both **Design Number** and **Item Number.** Even if you don't have the same color of a particular brick, as long as you have the same design, you'll be fine. Your model will just look a little different than the pictures in the workbook. Send pictures and we'll post them on our website!

## PURCHASING LEGO® BRICKS

There are two webpages you'll need to visit, both extensions of www.lego.com. Start with the Pick-A-Brick™ page. If the part is available through Pick-A-Brick™, you need to buy it there.

If not, go to the Bricks & Pieces™ page and you can get it there. On either Pick-A-Brick™ or Bricks & Pieces™ you can type in the **Item** or **Design Number and the site** will come up with the **part,** if it's available on that site. Add the quantity you need to your cart and continue that process for all the parts. It's easy and quick to order, although it might take a week or two for some parts to get to you—they may be coming all the way from Denmark! Please plan accordingly. The parts available on either site is always changing. On www.beakersandbricks.com, I'll keep an updated list of the best options for these parts, and screenshots on how this is done.

On the experiment list of supplies is also a length of string, a rubber band, and a short wooden dowel. These you can obtain yourself at a hobby or craft store, or you can purchase them from www.beakersandbricks.com.

## WEBSITE ADDRESSES

Pick-A-Brick™: https://www.lego.com/en-us/page/static/pick-a-brick

Bricks & Pieces™: https://www.lego.com/en-us/service/replacementparts

## BRICKS & PIECES™

| Part Name | Color | Item Number | Design Number | Quantity Needed | Part Picture |
|---|---|---|---|---|---|
| Technic 7M Beam | blue | 4506043 | 32524 | 4 | |
| Technic 3M Beam | blue | 4509376 | 32523 | 2 | |
| Connector peg W. Friction 3M | blue | 4514553 | 6558 | 9 | |
| Beam 1x1 | gray | 6100030 | 18654 | 3 | |
| Tube Wdouble 04.85 | light gray | 4526985 | 62462 | 2 | |
| Beam R.Frame 5x11 04.85 | light gray | 4540797 | 64178 | 2 | |
| beam 3M. W/4 SNAPS | gray | 4225033 | 48989 | 2 | |
| Angular Beam 90Degr. W.4 snaps | gray | 4296059 | 55615 | 2 | |
| Rim Narrow 018x7 W Hole 04.8 | light gray | 6044729 | 13971 | 4 | |
| Double Cross Block | light gray | 4211621 | 32184 | 2 | |
| DOUBLE CONICAL WHEEL Z20 1M | tan | 6084724 | 18575 | 2 | |
| TECHNIC ANG. BEAM 4X2 90 DEG | light gray | 4211610 | 32140 | 4 | |
| Universal Joint | light gray | 4525904 | 61903 | 4 | |
| 2x1x3 Steering Knuckle Arm | light gray | 4563045 | 33299 | 1 | |
| cross axle 12M | black | 370826 | 3708 | 2 | |

| Part Name | Color | Item Number | Design Number | Quantity Needed | Part Picture |
|---|---|---|---|---|---|
| Technic Lever 3M | black | 4107828 | 6632 | 2 | |
| Angle Element, 180 Degrees (2) | black | 4107783 | 32034 | 2 | |
| Cross Blok 3M | black | 4173970 | 42003 | 2 | |
| Worm | light gray | 4211510 | 4716 | 1 | |
| Cross Axle, Extension, 2M | red | 4513174 | 59443 | 1 | |
| Spool 0 15,83 x 7,99 | light gray | 4521532 | 61510 | 1 | |
| Gear Wheel Z24 | gray | 6133119 | 24505 | 3 | |
| Gear Wheel T=8, M=1 | gray | 6012451 | 10928 | 2 | |
| Toothed Bar M=1, Z=10 | light gray | 4211450 | 3743 | 2 | |
| Gear Wheel 40T | light gray | 4285634 | 3649 | 2 | |
| Technic Lever 4M | light gray | 4211561 | 32006 | 2 | |
| TECHNIC ANG. BEAM 3X5 90 DEG. | white | 4585040 | 32526 | 2 | |
| Cross Axle 3M | light gray | 4211815 | 4519 | 4 | |
| Plate 1x10 | blue | 447723 | 4477 | 1 | |
| Plate 6x8 | blue | 303623 | 3036 | 2 | |

## PICK-A-BRICK™

| Part Name | Color | Item Number | Design Number | Quantity Needed | Part Picture |
|---|---|---|---|---|---|
| Technic 15M beam | blue | 6057799 | 64871 | 15 | |
| Technic Brick 1x2, 04.9 | red | 3700021 | 3700 | 2 | |
| Technic Brick 1x2, 04.9 | blue | 3700023 | 3700 | 2 | |
| HUB 011,2 x 7,84 | light gray | 4211758 | 42610 | 1 | |
| Connector peg W. Friction | black | 4121715 | 2780 | 41 | |
| 1/2 bush | light gray | 4211573 | 32123 | 8 | |
| Connector Peg | light gray | 4211807 | 3673 | 1 | |
| bush for cross axle | light gray | 4211622 | 6590 | 14 | |
| Plate 2x4 | dark gray | 4211065 | 3020 | 2 | |
| TECHNIC ANG. BEAM 3X5 90 DEG. | gray | 4211713 | 32526 | 1 | |
| Cross Axle 4M | black | 370526 | 3705 | 3 | |
| Cross Axle 6M | black | 370626 | 3706 | 5 | |
| Cross Axle 8M | black | 370726 | 3707 | 1 | |
| 1 1/2 M Connecting Bush | tan | 6013938 | 32002 | 4 | |

| Part Name | Color | Item Number | Design Number | Quantity Needed | Part Picture |
|---|---|---|---|---|---|
| Double Conical Wheel Z12 1M | black | 4177431 | 32270 | 3 | |
| Connector Peg/Cross Axle | tan | 4666579 | 6562 | 2 | |
| Brick 2x4 | red | 300121 | 3001 | 32 | |
| Brick 2x2 | red | 300321 | 3003 | 2 | |
| Brick 2x8 | red | 6036408 | 93888 | 6 | |

| NON LEGO® ITEMS | Quantity | Part Picture |
|---|---|---|
| 2 3/16" long wood dowel, 3/4" to 1" in diameter, preferably oak or similarly dense wood | 1 | |
| Micro paracord 1.18mm in diameter | 64 inches | |
| 3 1/2" x 1/4" rubber band | 1 | |

# CHAPTER 1
# PHYSICS AND ENGINEERING BASICS

**This first chapter presents scientific information** you need before we get to the LEGO® brick models. Please work your way through it—it's worth the effort!

## PHYSICS AND ENGINEERING DEFINED

What's physics? Why is it important? What does a physicist do? How about engineering? Why isn't that word spelled with two N's? (In my opinion, it should be spelled "enginneering.") What do engineers do?

Let's answer these questions, with the exception of the spelling question. Apparently that's just the way it is...says my editor.

### Physics

Below is one definition of physics:

> *The branch of science concerned with the nature and properties of matter and energy. The subject matter of physics includes mechanics, heat, light and other radiation, sound, electricity, magnetism, and the structure of atoms.*[2]

More simply, physics deals with things that can be measured, like speed, acceleration, gravity, and directional forces, to name a few. Physics explains much of what we see and experience in the world around us.

An example can illustrate and help with your understanding:

Cars on a freeway[3]

You're riding in the backseat of a car, driven by Bob, moving along at 55 miles per hour (mph). You've been going straight and steady at that speed for some time. You don't experience anything—it feels like you're simply sitting in your seat with a mild hum from the road noise and a little vibration. Bob negotiates a tight turn to the left without slowing down to the recommended 40 mph speed. Your body is "pulled" to the right, it seems. You will probably even end up leaning a bit in that direction.

Suddenly, a deer jumps out! Bob slams on the brakes, almost stopping, with the tires squealing. Luckily, he missed the deer. In that case, you felt yourself restrained by your seatbelt. Your head may have moved forward and down, as if it were trying to keep going.

Road hazard[4]

Now, concerned about drivers coming from behind, Bob hits the gas to speed up quickly. You feel yourself being pressed back into your seat. Pretty soon, though, the car is moving steady at 55 mph, and again you feel as if you're sitting still.

This simple example can be described in great detail using the laws of physics as we currently understand them.

Most likely you've played a video game or watched a movie that showed something being blown up by an explosion of some kind. Because blowing things up is expensive, directors and producers usually display such actions by using computer graphics (CG). Have you ever wondered how they do that? How they can make it look real? Sophisticated *physics engines* simulate what would really happen. This software uses a lot of mathematical computations to accomplish its work, which requires a powerful computer processor.

***Physics engines:*** Computer software that uses the laws of physics to mathematically determine how digital objects should appear to behave as if they were real.

Much of science, including physics and engineering, can use models that approximate, or *simulate*, a real-life situation. Previously, when computers were slow and very expensive, models were built at a small scale to test a new machine before building it full-sized. Today, much of this type of work is done using software that can simulate anything from the stresses in a steel part to collision failure predictions.

The point is that our understanding of principles that describe nature is good—in fact, good enough that we've been able to reduce them to mathematical equations. They, in turn, can predict what complex real-world interactions do quite accurately.

So, what are these rules? Let's explore some famous and simple examples.

**This video shows the use of Autodesk®[5], a popular simulation software package, to experiment with the stresses on an object. Different forces show up in the simulation as different colors. You won't understand everything, but it gives you an idea about how this type of software works.**
https://www.youtube.com/watch?v=toYt_KQyugM

## Newton's Laws

Isaac Newton, a native of England, lived from 1642–1727. He's famous for the laws that were named after him, which are among the most basic principles of physics. His achievements were so great that he was knighted, which is why he's known as Sir Isaac Newton. While Newton's laws of motion are famous, this scientist and mathematician also made extraordinary advancements in the field of optics, published *Principia Mathematica Philosophiae Naturalis* in 1687 (still considered one of the greatest scientific books ever written), formulated the universal law of gravitation, and invented calculus.[6] So if you're struggling with calculus, you know who to blame! (Believe it or not, calculus is pretty cool! It pulls together all types of math into something useful and powerful.)

Isaac Newton[7]

## Newton's First Law of Motion

Sometimes referred to as the law of inertia, Newton's first law of motion can be described this way:

> *An object continues to do whatever it's doing, unchanged, unless an outside force acts on it.*

Let's go back to our car ride example.

When you're riding in the car at an even speed, your body doesn't feel any outside forces. This situation is sometimes referred to as *dynamic equilibrium*. The seat is pushing up on you the same amount that you're pushing down on it. Neither the seatbelt nor seat back are exerting any force on you.

> ***Dynamic equilibrium:*** Objects moving in a straight line at constant speed.
> ***Static equilibrium:*** Objects at rest (not moving at all).

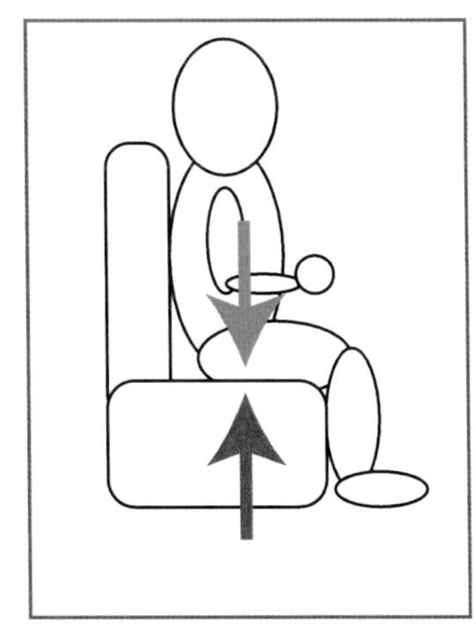

Equilibrium in a car

At this time, whenever the car *accelerates*, you feel pressure as you're pressed back into your seat. In this case, the ground pushes against the car, which in turn pushes against you.

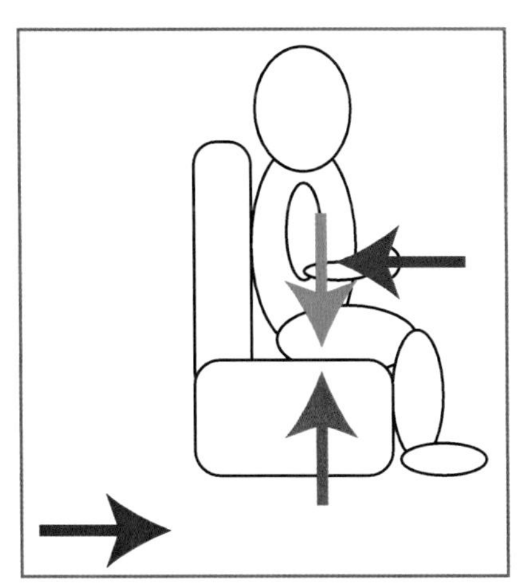

Acceleration in a car

The same happens for *deceleration*, in reverse. Similar pressures, or forces, are felt when the car is maneuvered through turns.

***Accelerate:*** Increasing speed.
***Decelerate:*** Reducing speed.

We feel the movement only because our body resists any change from equilibrium. This resistance is called "inertia." Think about a boulder. Unless a lot of force is applied, it's not going to move. It has a LOT of inertia. Similarly, a pebble isn't going to move either unless a force is applied. It just won't take as much force as the boulder.

## Newton's Second Law of Motion

This brings us to Newton's second law of motion, which is

commonly stated:

*Force = mass x acceleration*

To explain this law, we need to understand mass and acceleration.

### Mass

We talked about a boulder having a lot more inertia than a pebble. What makes the difference is *mass*. Mass isn't volume. For example, think of an empty box, and the same box full of books. Both boxes occupy the same volume, but have different mass.

Mass isn't weight, either, although in the same location, they're directly related. Consider our box of books if it were sitting on the moon vs. on Earth. On the moon, objects weigh approximately 1/6th what they do on Earth. A 50 lb. box of books on Earth weighs about 8.3 lbs. on the moon.

Perhaps the simplest way to think about mass is that it's *stuff*. It's a measure of inertia. The more stuff in an object, the more inertia it has, so the more resistant it is to changing its current state of equilibrium. Mass vs. weight is an important and difficult concept to grasp. Mass is measured using the kilogram (kg.) and the pound (lb.). Yes, this sounds like weight, but technically, it's not. More on this shortly.

**Astronauts bouncing on the moon. Keep in mind that their suits and equipment, when they're on Earth, weigh about 280 lbs.** [8]

https://www.youtube.com/watch?v=x2adl6LszcE

### Acceleration

To grasp *Force = mass x acceleration*, we also need to understand acceleration. Acceleration isn't a change in speed—it's the act of changing speed in a given amount of time:

*Acceleration = (Speed 2 – Speed 1) ÷ time*

Note that acceleration can be positive (if Speed 2 is greater than Speed 1) or negative (if Speed 2 is less than Speed 1). When it's negative, it's called "deceleration." Because speed is a measurement of distance per unit of time, such as feet per second, and the change in speed associated with acceleration is also measured over time, we end up with squared time, which is identified by a superscript 2 at the end of the formula. Squared time is another important but difficult concept to grasp. Consider that our car is moving at 55 miles per hour, and accelerates to 70 miles per hour in 5 seconds. Convert miles per hour (mph) to feet per second (ft./s).

Note that this requires an understanding of conversion of units, also called "stoichiometry."

***Stoichiometry:*** The methodical conversion of units from one form to another using established conversion factors. Performing this calculation carefully and in a step-by-step fashion reduces errors.

In order to get the proper units—in this case, feet per second—you have to multiply or divide by the conversion factor. We start with miles per hour. To convert miles into feet, we multiply by the known conversion factor of 5,280 feet per mile, resulting in feet per hour. To convert hours into seconds, we divide by the known conversion factor of 3,600 seconds per hour. Now we have what we want—feet per second. This can also be written in this manner. You may find it more helpful to write out the equation.

$$\left(\frac{55\ \cancel{Miles}}{\cancel{Hour}}\right) x \left(\frac{5{,}280\ Feet}{\cancel{Mile}}\right) x \left(\frac{1\ \cancel{Hour}}{3{,}600\ Seconds}\right) = \left(\frac{80.7\ Feet}{Second}\right)$$

$$\left(\frac{70\ \cancel{Miles}}{\cancel{Hour}}\right) x \left(\frac{5{,}280\ Feet}{\cancel{Mile}}\right) x \left(\frac{1\ \cancel{Hour}}{3{,}600\ Seconds}\right) = \left(\frac{102.7\ Feet}{Second}\right)$$

Acceleration can be calculated as follows:

$$Acceleration = \left(\frac{102.7\ Feet}{Second} - \frac{80.7\ Feet}{Second}\right) \div 5\ Seconds$$

$$Acceleration = \left(\frac{22\ Feet}{Second}\right) \div 5\ Seconds = \left(\frac{4.4\ Feet}{Second\ per\ Second}\right)$$

$$Or\ \left(\frac{4.4\ Feet}{Second^2}\right)$$

So when you think of acceleration, it's a change that's happening during every bit of time. The average acceleration was a 4.4 feet/second increase in speed for every passing second, for 5 seconds, at which point acceleration dropped to zero and the new constant speed was 102.7 feet/second.

## Back to the Second Law

With an understanding of mass and acceleration, we can define Newton's second law more accurately. In the section on mass, it was mentioned that kilograms and pounds are often used as measurements for weight. This works on Earth only because the acceleration component, which in this case is gravity, is a constant for all of us. More specifically, force is measured in *newtons* (yes, named after Sir Isaac), which units are kg·m/s2, as follows:

$$Force\ (newton) = Mass(Kilograms)\ x\ Acceleration\left(\frac{Meters}{Second^2}\right)$$

One kilogram on Earth (2.2 lbs.) is 10 newtons. Scientists, especially those dealing with changes in height, and particularly when you get into space, use newtons to describe weight because the acceleration component is no longer constant.

For example, remember the bouncing astronauts? How can they bounce when they're wearing a 280 lb. mass? The answer is, the force available for application through the action of moving their muscles is the same, or close to it, as if they were on Earth, while the weight is 1/6 of what it was on Earth. The 280 lb. weight is closer to 46 lbs. on the moon. Still not light, but much lighter than on Earth.

## G-Forces – The "Force" of Gravity: An Example of Acceleration

Let's look into gravity a little more. The pressure or force felt while accelerating or turning in a car, and in other scenarios, are sometimes referred to as *g-forces*. This requires a little bit of explanation.

Gravity affects all of us. We feel pressure on our feet while we're standing, or on our rear while we're sitting. Why isn't it like a car, when we feel it when accelerating or decelerating but not when we're moving in a straight line? The reason is because when we're under the effect of gravity, we're constantly accelerating. That is, gravity is constantly pulling on us—it never stops. This example of acceleration is called "the acceleration due to gravity." It has a value that can be measured, which on

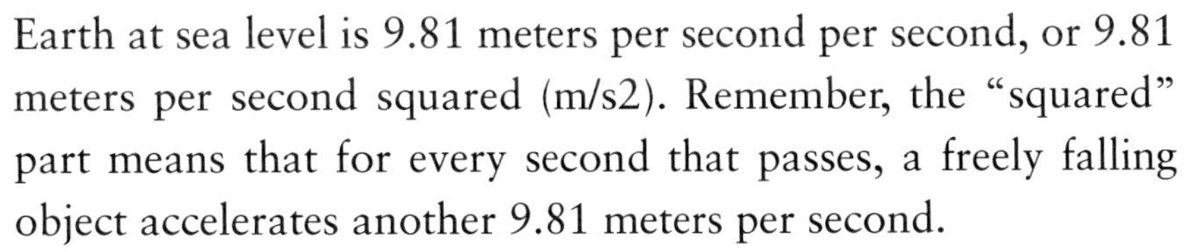

Earth at sea level is 9.81 meters per second per second, or 9.81 meters per second squared (m/s2). Remember, the "squared" part means that for every second that passes, a freely falling object accelerates another 9.81 meters per second.

In other words, 1 g-force is equal to 9.81 m/s2. It's a good thing we have gravity, as otherwise nothing would be held to Earth, ourselves and the atmosphere we breathe included.

**G-forces explained:**
https://www.youtube.com/watch?v=DMKcO-T5Y4o

Ferrari[9]

Toyota Corolla[10]

Let's look at another example of acceleration. Compare the time it takes to go from 0–60 mph in a Ferrari 488 Spider and a 2019 Toyota Corolla. The graph is fairly simplistic, as there would be some wiggle in the acceleration curve due to the type of transmission, any high-speed inefficiencies (particularly for the Toyota), etc.

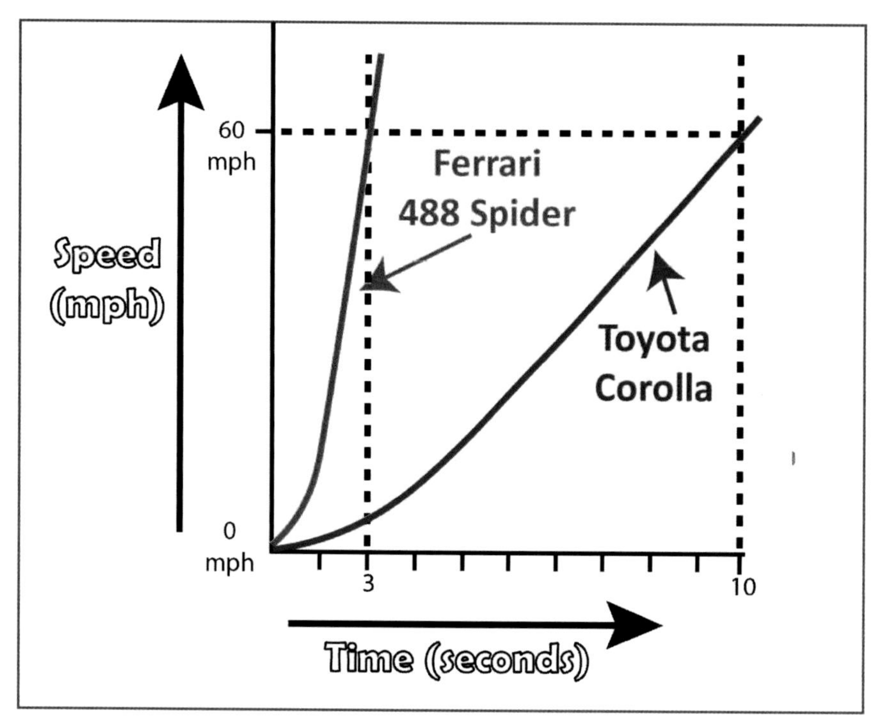


Ferrari vs. Corolla Acceleration[11]

Let's compare specifications of these two cars:

| | Toyota Corolla | Ferrari 488 Spider |
|---|---|---|
| Horsepower | 139 | 660 |
| Weight (lbs) | 3,045 | 3,131 |

While the cars aren't that much different in weight, the Ferrari has almost five times more horsepower than the Toyota, allowing it to accelerate much faster. In other words, the force available from the Ferrari's motor is greater than the force available from the Corolla's motor, while both are working on accelerating a similar mass. Rearranging the equation a little can aid your understanding:

*Acceleration = force ÷ mass*

The resulting g-forces, as felt by being "pressed" back into your seat, would be much higher in the Ferrari, as you can expect.

We can calculate the acceleration for both cars. First, convert miles per hour (miles/hour) to feet per second (feet/second):

$$\left(\frac{60\ Miles}{Hour}\right) x \left(\frac{5{,}280\ Feet}{HourMile}\right) x \left(\frac{1\ Hour}{3{,}600\ Seconds}\right) = \left(\frac{88\ Feet}{Second}\right)$$

Next, determine the acceleration for both, using the following formula:

*Acceleration = (final speed – beginning speed) ÷ time*

Convert into g-forces by dividing by the acceleration due to gravity, which is 9.81m/s2, or 32 ft./s2.

For the Ferrari:

$$\left(\frac{88\ Feet}{Second}\right) - \left(\frac{0\ Feet}{Second}\right) \div 3\ Seconds = \left(\frac{29.3\ ft.}{s^2}\right)$$

$$then$$

$$\left(\frac{29.3\ ft.}{s^2}\right) \div \left(\frac{32\ ft.}{s^2}\right) = 0.92\ G\ Force$$

***Unit conversions:*** It bears repeating that properly converting all the units is very important. I missed many test questions for failing to accomplish this task. It's much worse if you mess up the design of a machine!

In other words, you'd be pressed back in your seat by almost 1 g-force.

For the Corolla:

$$\left(\frac{88\ Feet}{Second}\right) - \left(\frac{0\ Feet}{Second}\right) \div 10\ Seconds = \left(\frac{8.8\ ft.}{s^2}\right)$$

$$then$$

$$\left(\frac{8.8\ ft.}{s^2}\right) \div \left(\frac{32\ ft.}{s^2}\right) = 0.28\ G\ Force$$

So what does this mean? An average human head weighs 10 lbs. If you have 0.92 of g-forces pressing your head back into the seat, it would be about 9.2 lbs. of force in the Ferrari. In the Corolla, it would be about 2.8 lbs. of force. If you have one, pick up a 10 lb. weight. It doesn't sound like much, but it's pretty heavy! You'd certainly feel it if you were lying on the floor and someone put a 10 lb. weight on your head. (Please don't do this.)

### Newton's Third Law of Motion

The third law says: for every action there is an equal and opposite reaction. Most of us have heard this phrase, but do we understand what the actual law means? Let's go back to our car example. Direct evidence of this principle can be seen when the car accelerates: we experience being pushed back into our seat. Look again:

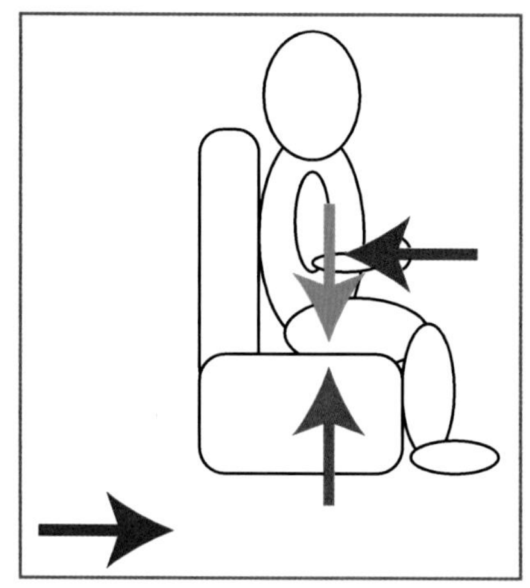

Acceleration in a car

The ground pushes against the car as the car pushes against the ground. In turn, you push against the car seat as the car seat pushes against you. Stated in other words, the car is the first force, taking action by pushing against the ground. The ground reacts by pushing against the car. Since the ground doesn't move, the car moves forward.

## Conservation of Energy

Another important concept is the fact that energy can't be created or destroyed, only moved around or balanced. This concept is similar to and is related to Newton's laws of motion.

## Motion in One and Two Dimensions

We've talked quite a bit about forces making things move. While this workbook doesn't get into it in detail, it bears mentioning that the topic can become pretty complex. When talking about a moving object, we talk about *speed* and *velocity*. Most people think these terms mean the same thing, but they don't!

*Speed = distance ÷ time*
*Velocity = distance ÷ time + direction*

The answer to the question, "How fast were you going?" doesn't answer *where* you were going. Maybe it doesn't matter, but usually direction is important. For example, you won't get to class on time, even leaving early and traveling fast, if you travel in the wrong direction.

### Work

Work is force over (multiplied by) distance traveled:

*Work = force x distance*

Look carefully and think about that formula, because it has a lot of bearing on machines and how they work. If you're going to move an object from one point to another, the amount of work needed is the same no matter how you get it there. What is different is the amount of force and the total distance traveled. If the distance increases, the force needed to produce the same amount of work is less. If the force increases, the distance needed is reduced.

For example, we will look at ramps, or inclined planes, in a later chapter. It takes less force to push a barrel up a ramp than it does to hoist it straight up to get to the same point, but the ramp is a longer distance.

> ***Simple machines:*** The inclined plane, the lever, the pulley, the screw, the wedge, and the wheel and axle are generally considered to be the six simple machines. Some are closely related and are frequently grouped together when referenced in textbooks. For example, the inclined plane, the wedge, and the screw are all inclined planes, but in some texts they are treated separately.
> ***Complex machines:*** Two or more simple machines constructed together in one machine. For example, a wheelbarrow is a combination of a lever and the wheel and axle. A common can opener has levers, wheels and axles, and an inclined plane.

## Engineering

Engineering is applying scientific knowledge when building things that are useful. Bridges, tools of all kinds, roads, etc.—pretty much everything you see and use—have been engineered in some fashion to be useful and help make tasks easier, or even possible. The LEGO® brick machines we will build in this workbook are all examples of engineering.

Referring back to the concept of *Work = force x distance*, in most instances, increasing distance to reduce the needed force is the primary concept in simple machines.

For example, pushing an object up a ramp results in moving the object a longer distance than lifting it straight up, but the amount of force needed to push it up the ramp is much less than lifting it straight up. A ramp is an inclined plane, an example of a simple machine that we'll discuss in more detail later.

Multiple simple machines used together in the same machine make up a *complex machine*. Most of the LEGO® brick machines we will construct in this workbook are complex machines, designed to demonstrate a simple machine concept.

## EXPERIMENTS: LET'S BUILD SOMETHING!

### Basics Experiment #1: Distance Traveled vs. Distance Falling #1

***Caution:*** *This experiment involves making a launcher, which could launch things at pets or siblings. Please be careful to avoid injury, and certainly don't aim the launcher at any living thing!*

#### Parts Needed:

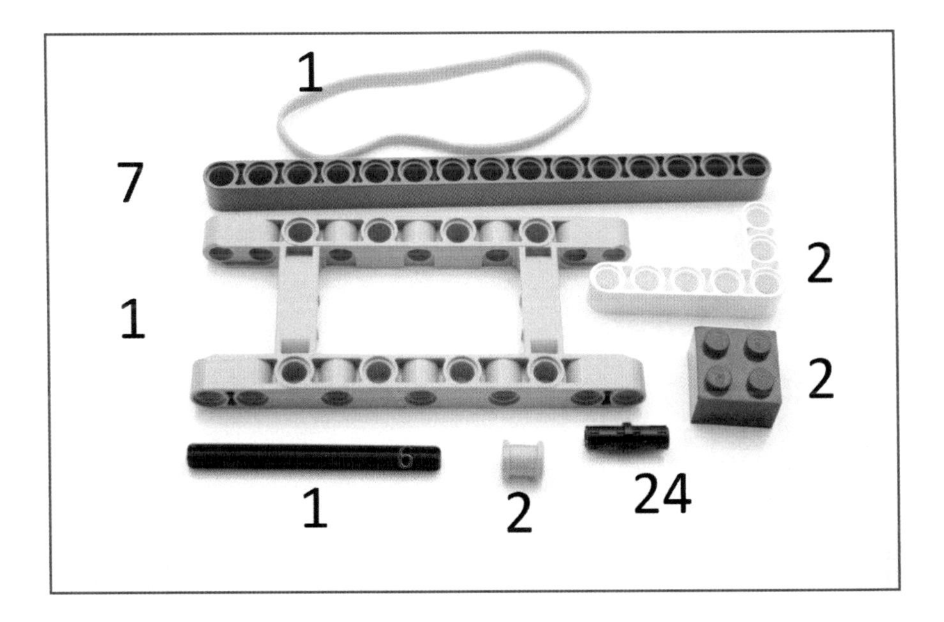


#### Procedures:

1. Build the launcher.

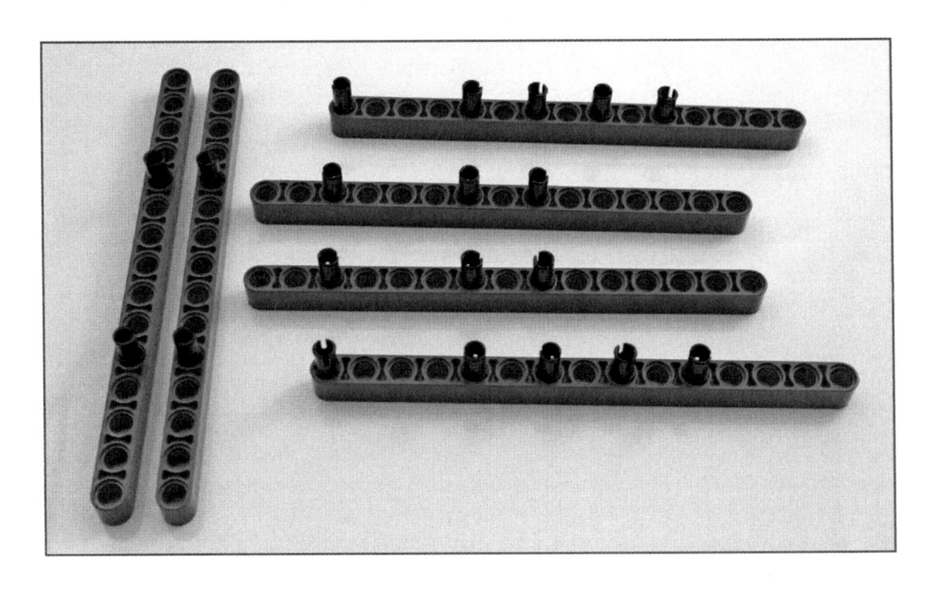

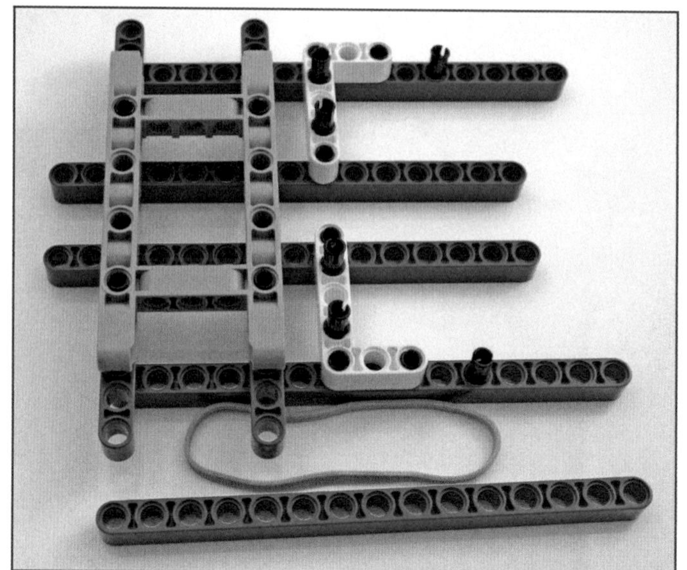

2. Place the launcher on a flat, smooth, elevated surface, such as a table. The higher the surface the better. It needs to be safely accessible, flat, and smooth.
3. Hold the launcher as shown, near the table's edge, and pull the firing pin.

4. How long does it take for the piece to hit the floor? This part works best if you are over a hard floor so you can hear the projectile hit the floor. The time will be very short, so you won't be able to count the time, but by listening carefully to when the projectile hits, and re-

peating, you will be able to recognize the time changes. Repeat Steps 4 and 5 several times.

5. Now place the projectile in the slot, as shown. Carefully move the launcher to the table's side until the projectile falls. How much time does it take for it to hit the floor?

6. Write down your observations.

7. If you have the ability to try the experiment at a different level, do so—like from the top of a fridge, a bookshelf, etc. Repeat Steps 2 through 5 on the new surfaces and record your observations.

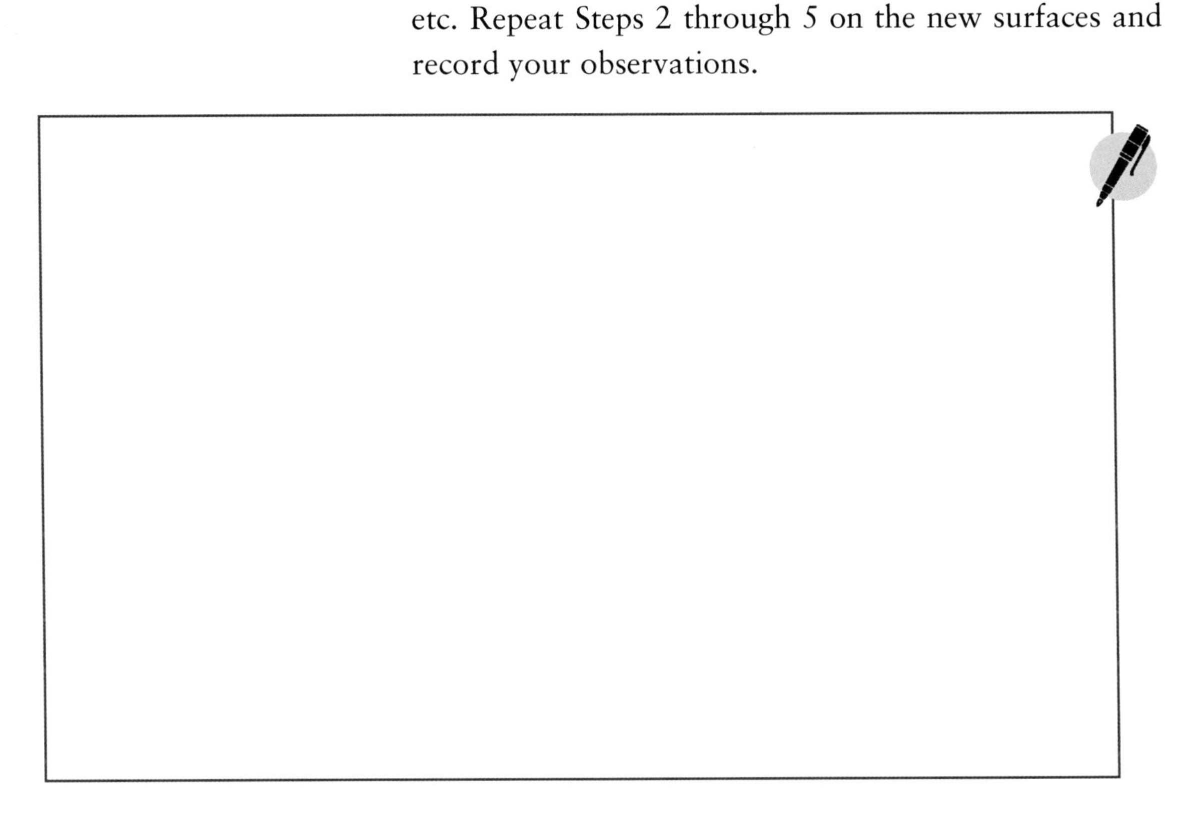

### Basics Experiment #1: Distance Traveled vs. Distance Falling #1 Discussion

The projectile is acted upon constantly by acceleration due to gravity. Gravity's effect holds true whether the projectile is moving forward or falling straight down. As long as no other force acts on the projectile during its flight, it hits the floor in exactly the same amount of time as when it's dropped straight down, when traveling from the same surface. The same happens if a bullet is shot from a gun parallel to the ground but it travels a long distance before it strikes something. This experiment demonstrates the constant acceleration of gravity, regardless of whether an object is moving or not.

## Basics Experiment #2: Distance Traveled vs. Distance Falling #2

### Parts Needed:

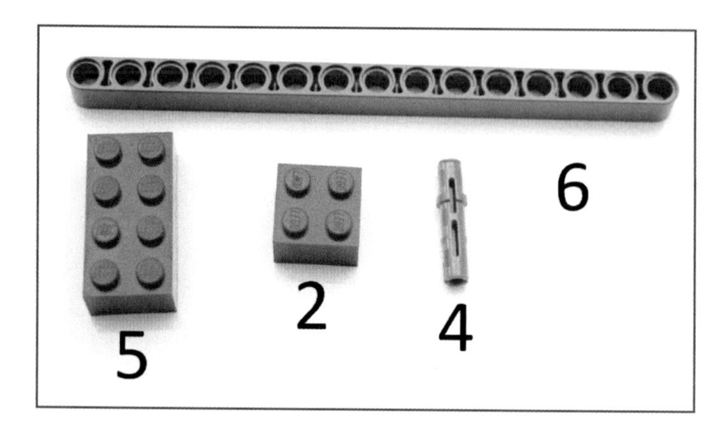


### Procedures:

This experiment is pretty simple and will give you a good idea of what Air Force pilots had to deal with in World War II.

1. Build the drop machine.

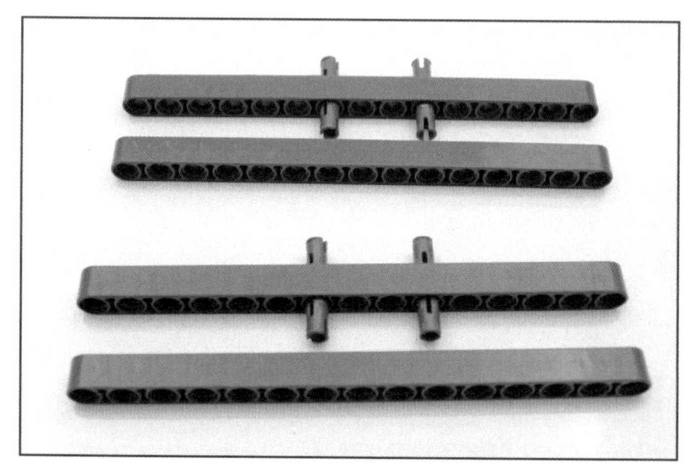

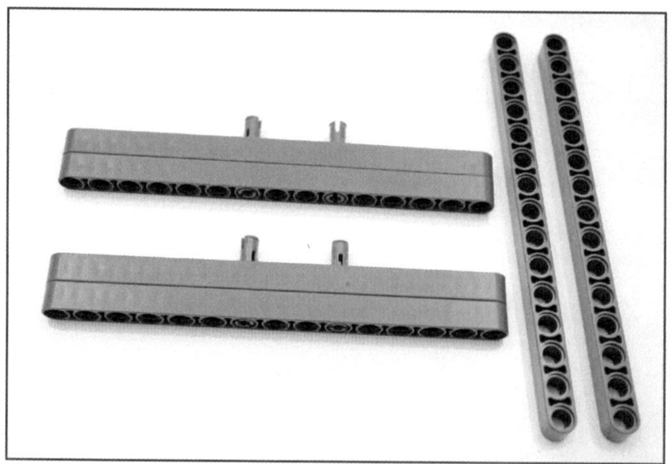

2. Make a bull's-eye target by drawing circles on a sheet of paper.

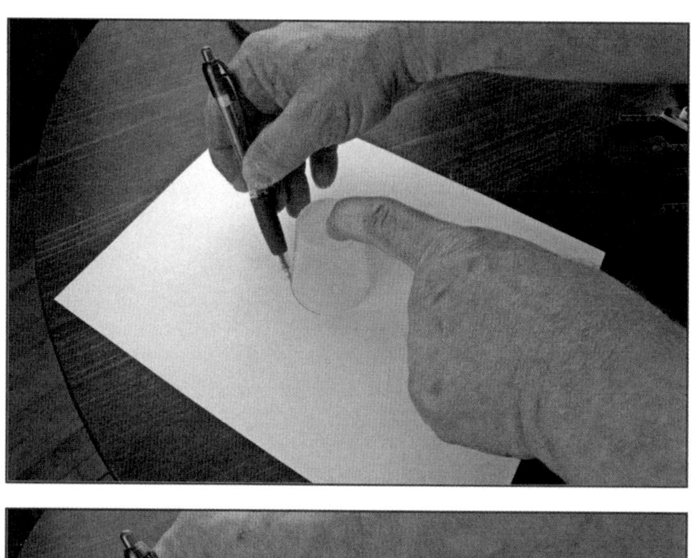

3. Place the target on the floor in a clear area.
4. Hold the drop machine up to your eye as shown, with the

bomb in place.

5. Stand over the target and drop the bomb repeatedly on the target until you have your "targeting eye" calibrated to hit the bull's-eye (target center) regularly.
6. Now stand a few feet in front of the target, hold the drop machine and bomb up to your eye again as before, and walk toward the target slowly. Drop the bomb and try to hit the target while you're still moving. Record your observations.

7. Continue until you're reasonably accurate at hitting the target.

### Basics Experiment #2: Distance Traveled vs. Distance Falling #2 Discussion

You probably found that hitting the target was much more difficult when you were moving. The bomb dropped in the same amount of time, but continued to move forward at the same speed you were walking when it was dropped. Dropping bombs is an example of inertia, Newton's first law.

Now think about what other factors would come into play if you were really trying to hit a target from an aircraft: high speeds, crosswinds over the target, and other factors. World War II bombers were equipped with special sights that took into account as many factors such as these as could be accounted for. It's amazing they hit anywhere close to their targets!

World War II bomber sighting equipment[12]

**A calculation explanation associated with targeting objects on the ground from planes:**
https://www.youtube.com/watch?v=CzlQ104Qfb0

## WHAT DO YOU THINK?

**Several different concepts were presented in this chapter, some of which were likely new to you. Finding novel ways to learn and demonstrate that learning is often how new discoveries are made.**

**Let's return to our astronauts on the moon. Many conveniences we enjoy today are directly related to research conducted to make the moon landing possible, including cordless tools, the CAT scanner, and the procedures that food production facilities cur-**

**rently use to keep our food safe, called HACCP (Hazard Analysis Critical Control Points).**

## JOURNALING IDEA

Pretend you're living in a time prior to Isaac Newton and other great scientists. You're a budding scientist yourself, trying to figure out how to demonstrate that objects fall at the same rate. What would you do?

## CHAPTER REVIEW

1. We illustrated that when a car accelerates, the car pushes against the ground and the ground pushes back against the car. Since the ground doesn't move, the car moves forward. Can you think of an example where the car might not move forward?
2. Make a chart using *Force = mass x acceleration*, keeping the mass at 1 kg. and changing the acceleration from 1 to 25 m/s2 in steps of five. What does the resulting force data tell you?
3. From the chart you constructed in Example 2, what would happen if the force and mass remained the same while the acceleration decreased?
4. Imagine you're parachuting out of a plane. You fall quickly and then deploy your parachute, slowing to a constant, safe rate of descent. This constant rate of descent is called the "terminal velocity," or the velocity at which the upward force from the air resistance on the parachute equals the downward force of the combined weight of you and your equipment. What other factors come into play? When would terminal velocity never occur (think of outer space)?
5. Can you think of a modification to the drop machine that would improve your ability to hit the target? Another way to put this: Is there any way to engineer the drop machine to improve its accuracy?

# CHAPTER 2
# SIMPLE MACHINES: THE LEVER

## CONSERVATION OF ENERGY

**You are already familiar** with the law of conservation of energy and you didn't even know it! This principle states:

*Energy can't be lost or destroyed, only changed from one form to another.*

***Potential energy:*** Energy that's available in a system—whether it be mechanical (elastic or gravitational) or chemical—that is ready to be transformed into kinetic energy.
***Kinetic energy:*** The energy of a moving object, or the work being performed by the moving object.

Think of energy as being moved from one place to another. A classic example is a bow being pulled back, creating *potential energy,* which is transferred to the arrow in flight as *kinetic energy.* Another example is a ball rolled to the top of a hill. While sitting at the hill's top, it has potential energy, which is reduced as it rolls down the hill.

Potential energy in a bow[13]

Machines can store energy as well. In industrial work situations, workers are taught to release all the potential energy from a machine before getting themselves in a position where any of that pent-up energy could be released on their bodies, causing injury. Most workplaces have specific procedures to ensure that all the stored energy is released and the machines are "locked out" to avoid renergization.

***My huge oak tree:***

Author's downed oak tree[14]

In June 2019, I (pictured with my son, Stephen) had an approximate 175-year-old oak fall across my driveway. A primary concern as we worked to clear the large, heavy limbs was potential energy. Cutting through a limb could cause either the limb or the whole trunk to shift, roll, and/or fall in unexpected ways. We didn't want anyone in the way as the potential energy was converted into kinetic energy. Great care was taken with machinery and rigging to ensure that the cuts would be made safely. It was still scary at times, with cuts made cautiously and with escape routes planned and accessible. It was a great relief when the main trunk was on the ground and potential energy had been reduced to near zero!

**Dale's Oak Tree Disposal: If you'd like to see a video of me, my wife, and my youngest son taking care of this tree, it is at:** https://www.youtube.com/watch?v=0pHtvypiCHE

Energy can also be stored chemically, which can contain great amounts of potential energy. When chemical systems are properly set up, the release can be large. Batteries are a good case, while other examples are a stick of dynamite, or even a nuclear fission bomb. Kinetic energy, indeed!

Nuclear blast[15]

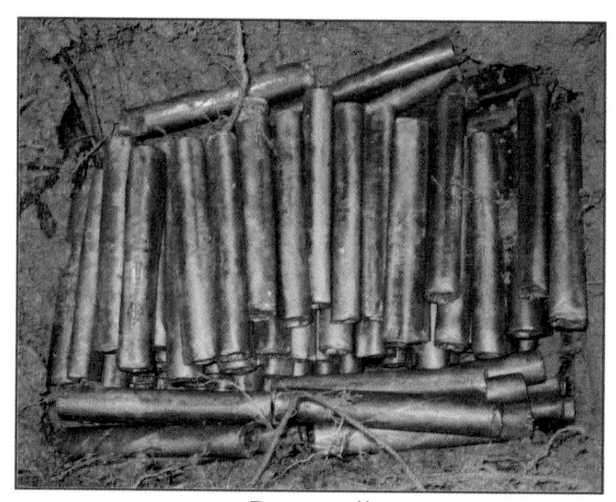

Dynamite[16]

## LEVER TYPES

One simple machine is the lever. Three types, or classes, of levers exist. Let's take a look at each one, but first, some terminology:

All levers have two main components: (A) the lever (usually a straight object) where the effort and load forces are applied, and (B) the fulcrum or the pivot point. The fulcrum's location in relation to the effort and load forces is what defines the class of lever.

### First-Class Levers

First-class levers have the fulcrum between the mass and the applied force.

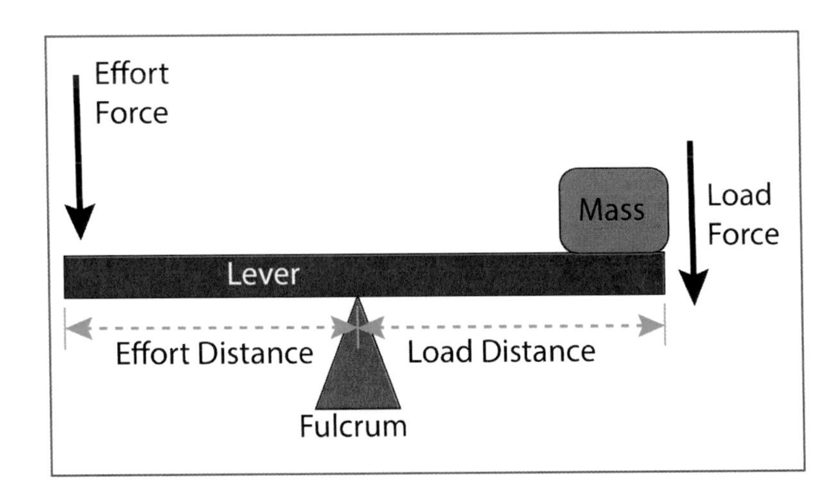


***All around you:*** As you learn about levers, pay attention to your daily activities. You'll quickly see that most everything you do involves using a lever of some sort, either part of your body, or through the use of a machine.

Examples of first-class levers are all around us:

- The playground see-saw
- A pry bar, such as the claw part of a hammer
- Scissors
- Pliers
- They even occur in nature: your head pivots on your neck as you nod.

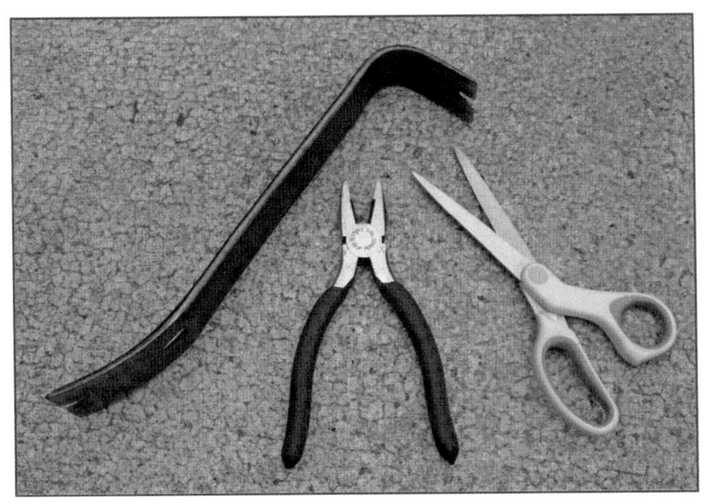

Pry bar, scissors, pliers

So how does this work? Let's use a pry bar as an example, such as the one pictured. As force is applied to the lever (one end of the pry bar), the pry bar pivots on the fulcrum and moves the load end. In other words, one end of the pry bar moves in one direction while the load end moves in the opposite direction. For instance, the load end may be trying to remove a nail from a board. With the fulcrum near the load, the long lever arm (hammer handle) magnifies the effort force. This magnification is called "mechanical advantage." Let's make some calculations:

*Effort force x effort distance = load force x load distance*

We know because of conservation of energy, both sides of the equation must be equal. Let's give some numbers to this and make a table, calculating the load force and mechanical advantage.

*Load force = (effort force x effort distance) ÷ load distance*

and

*Mechanical advantage = load force ÷ effort force*

The effort force = 10 newtons, and the lever length = 10 meters. Note: Mechanical advantage is by definition unit-less. Let's incrementally change the fulcrum's location from 1 meter toward the effort side, to 1/2 meter from the load side.

**A little boy explaining first class levers:**
https://www.youtube.com/watch?v=YuHZg0F18GA

| Effort Distance | Load Distance | Effort Force | Load Force | Mechanical Advantage |
|---|---|---|---|---|
| 1 | 9 | 10 | 1.1 | 0.1 |
| 2 | 8 | 10 | 2.5 | 0.3 |
| 3 | 7 | 10 | 4.3 | 0.4 |
| 4 | 6 | 10 | 6.7 | 0.7 |
| 5 | 5 | 10 | 10.0 | 1.0 |
| 6 | 4 | 10 | 15.0 | 1.5 |
| 7 | 3 | 10 | 23.3 | 2.3 |
| 8 | 2 | 10 | 40.0 | 4.0 |
| 9 | 1 | 10 | 90.0 | 9.0 |
| 9.5 | 0.5 | 10 | 190.0 | 19.0 |

Notice how the load force resulting from the same 10 newton effort force steadily goes up, then dramatically increases as the fulcrum approaches the load force end. Pry bars are designed with the fulcrum (where the iron bends, making a built-in fulcrum) very close to the tool's load end. It's pretty amazing! A 10 newton effort force results in 190 newtons of load force. The graph really helps to demonstrate what's going on.

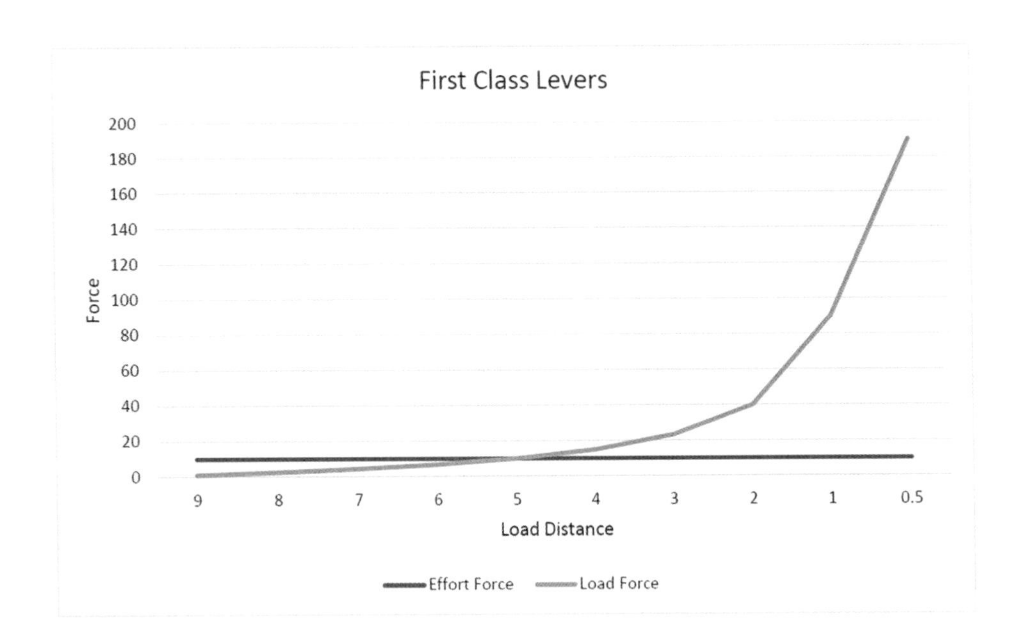


First-class levers are effective, but they don't work in every situation.

## Second-Class Levers

Second-class levers move the fulcrum to one end of the lever, with the load force between the effort force and the fulcrum.

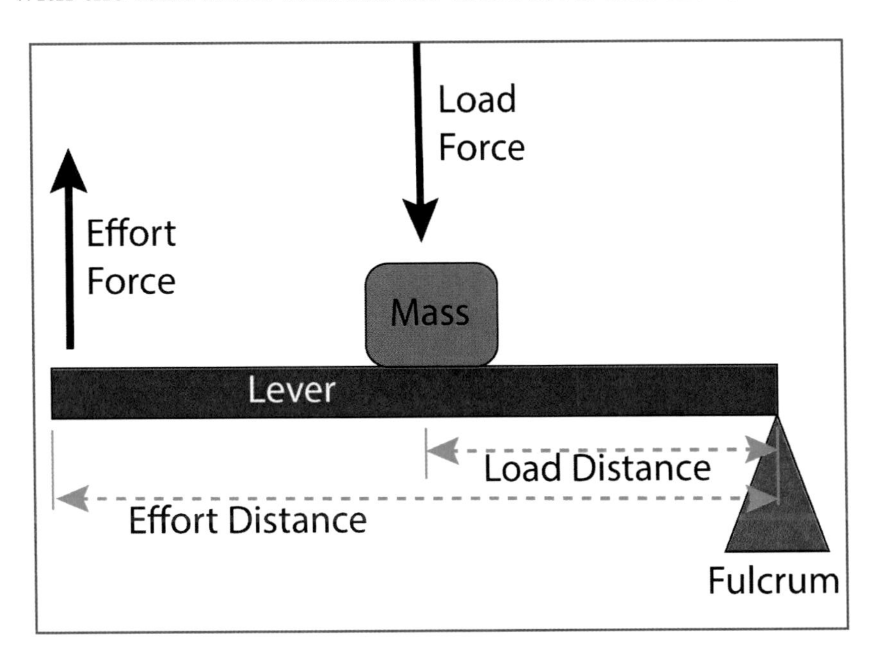

Examples of second-class levers include:

- The wheelbarrow

Wheelbarrow

**The same little boy explaining second-class levers:** https://www.youtube.com/watch?v=5H8flw-Ub6M

- A paper cutter

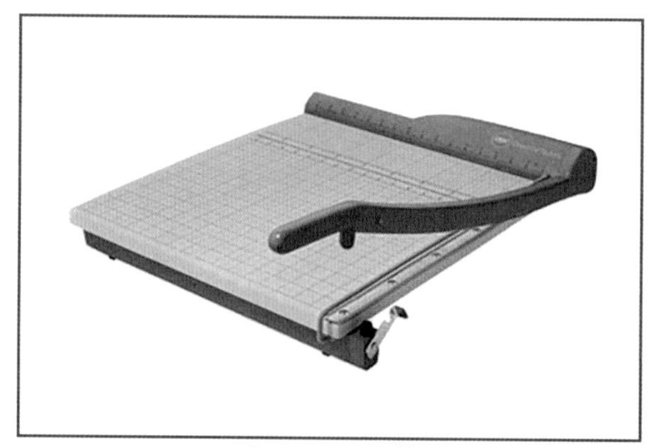

Paper cutter[17]

- A nutcracker

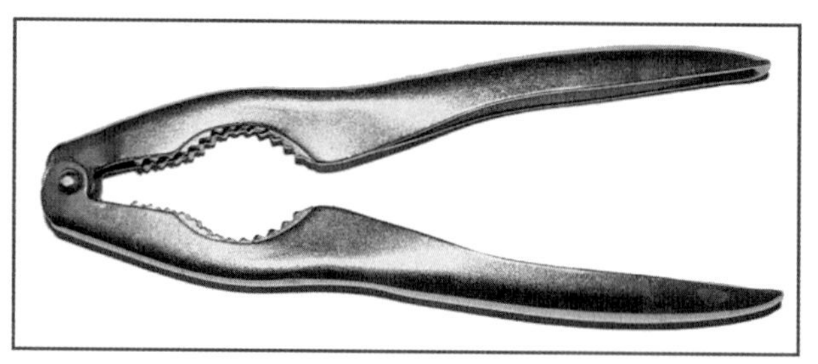

Nutcracker[18]

- Others include a bottle cap remover and, in our bodies, the ankle joint.

The formula is the same, but it's used a little differently:

*Effort distance x effort force = load distance x load force*

This time, we'll calculate the amount of force required to balance the load, as otherwise you'd dump the wheelbarrow! Rearrange the formula as follows:

*Effort force = (load distance x load force) ÷ effort distance*

Let's say we have a 50 lb. bag of concrete mix in the wheelbarrow, a load distance of 1 foot, and an effort distance of 4 feet:

*Effort force = 1 ft. x 50 lbs. ÷ 4 ft. = 12.5 lbs. force required to balance the 50 lb. load 1 ft. from the fulcrum*

The mechanical advantage can be calculated:

*Mechanical advantage = load force ÷ effort force = 50 lbs. ÷ 12.5 lbs. = 4*

Note: These are proportional formulas. The units don't really matter, whether they are newtons, pounds, feet, meters, etc.—as long you don't mix them.

Let's run a table again, moving the load away from the fulcrum and toward the effort location.

| Effort Distance | Load Distance | Effort Force | Load Force | Mechanical Advantage |
|---|---|---|---|---|
| 4 | 1 | 12.5 | 50.0 | 4.0 |
| 4 | 2 | 25.0 | 50.0 | 2.0 |
| 4 | 3 | 37.5 | 50.0 | 1.3 |
| 4 | 3.5 | 43.8 | 50.0 | 1.1 |
| 4 | 3.9 | 48.8 | 50.0 | 1.0 |

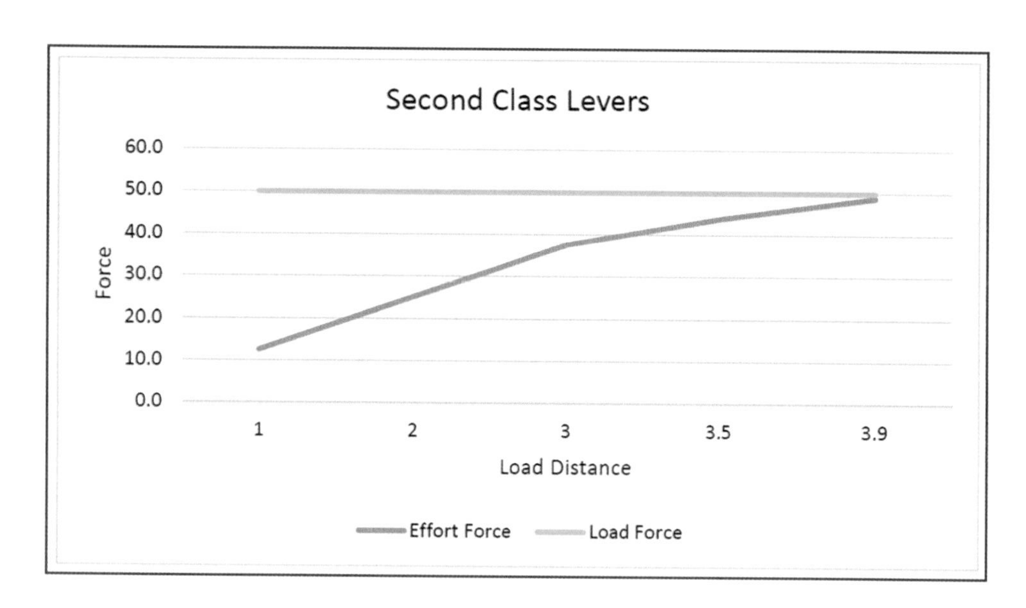


You can see from the table and graph that the effect is very different for first- and second-class levers. We'll revisit this in an experiment.

## Third-Class Levers

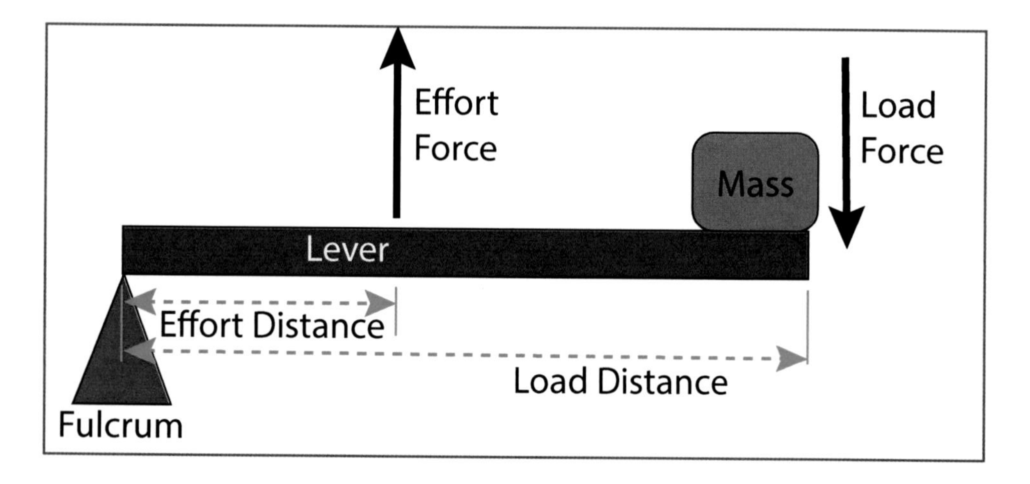


Yet another type of lever moves the effort force between the fulcrum and the load force. We can perform calculations associated with third-class levers as well, with the same formula:

*Effort force x effort distance = load force x load distance*

In this case, let's find out the force required to balance the load again. We need to calculate the force that has to be exceeded to move the load. We'll use a 50 lb. load and a lever with a total length of 10 ft. We'll start with the load force being applied at 3 ft. from the fulcrum.

> *Effort force = (load force x load distance) ÷ effort distance*

> *Effort force = (50 lb. x 5 ft.) ÷ 3 ft. = 83.3 lbs.*

So we find an interesting thing about third-class levers: the effort force must be equal to or greater than the load force. If the effort force is greater than the load force, no mechanical advantage exists. So why do they exist? The answer is in where the tool can reach and what it can do. In some cases, having to use more force rather than lifting the load straight up is acceptable, because it allows us to extend our reach.

Examples of this type of lever include:

- Excavation equipment

Excavation shovel[19]

**An fun explanation of leverage and simple machines:**
https://www.youtube.com/watch?v=YlYEi0PgG1g

- Tweezers

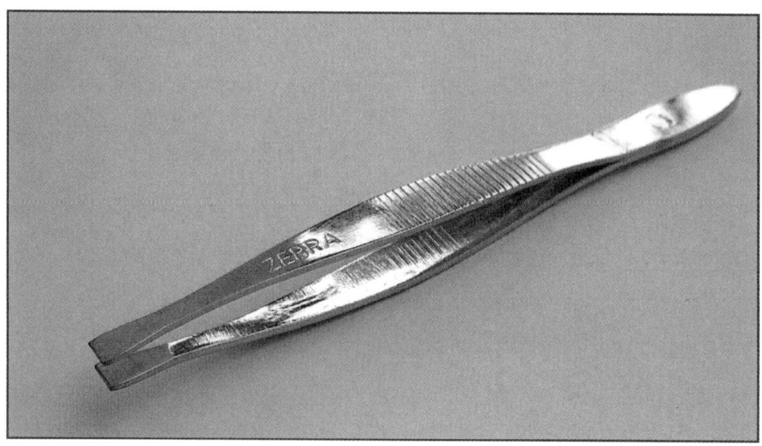


Tweezers[20]

A broom, fishing rod, and the bicep muscle's action on the forearm are other examples of third-class levers. In fact, if you start to look around, third-class levers are everywhere, in machines and also in animals, including humans!

In third-class levers, the load is always at the end of the lever arm, and the fulcrum is always at the other end. The variable is where the effort force is applied.

| Effort Distance | Load Distance | Effort Force | Load | Mechanical Advantage |
|---|---|---|---|---|
| 1 | 10 | 500.0 | 50.0 | 0.1 |
| 2 | 10 | 250.0 | 50.0 | 0.2 |
| 3 | 10 | 166.7 | 50.0 | 0.3 |
| 4 | 10 | 125.0 | 50.0 | 0.4 |
| 5 | 10 | 100.0 | 50.0 | 0.5 |
| 6 | 10 | 83.3 | 50.0 | 0.6 |
| 7 | 10 | 71.4 | 50.0 | 0.7 |
| 8 | 10 | 62.5 | 50.0 | 0.8 |
| 9 | 10 | 55.6 | 50.0 | 0.9 |
| 10 | 10 | 50.0 | 50.0 | 1.0 |

**Awesome video of a large excavator with a third-class lever on the final arm. Try to get a sense of scale here by noting the stairs and ladders to get to the operator cabs. These machines are HUGE!**

https://www.youtube.com/watch?v=vLNayfMsNol

A graph can help clarify how this works:

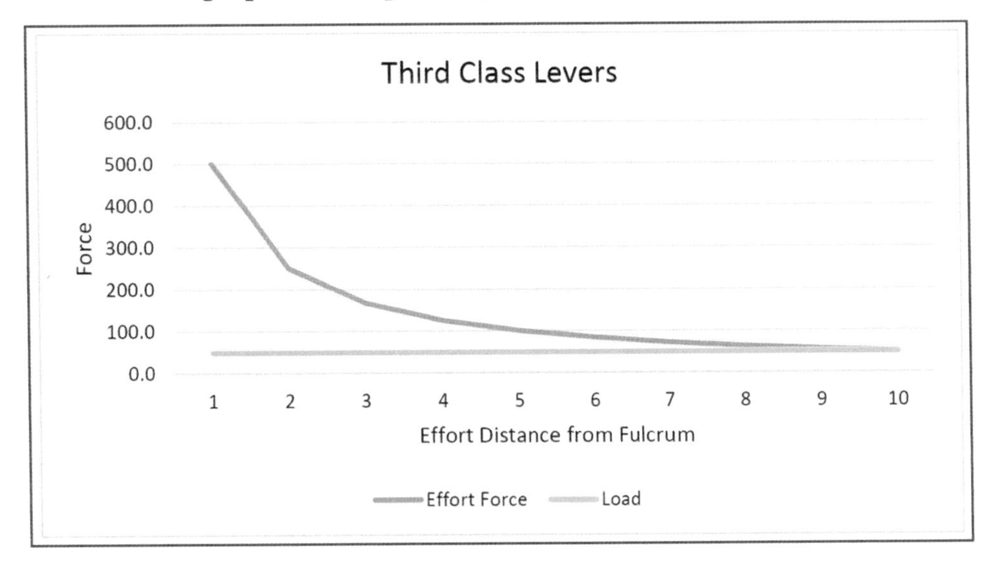


It can take a lot of force to move an object when the effort is applied close to the pivot point in a third-class type of lever system. If you haven't already, watch an excavation equipment video. The amount of force applied by those hydraulic cylinders, also called "hydraulic rams," to move the huge shovels full of dirt and rock is enormous!

**A great review of levers, including examples in the human body:**
https://www.youtube.com/watch?v=eTa2EFd3JF0

## EXPERIMENTS: LET'S BUILD SOMETHING!

### Levers Experiment #1: First-Class Levers

Remember: in first-class levers, the fulcrum is between the mass and the force. Think of a see-saw or a pry bar.

### Parts Needed:

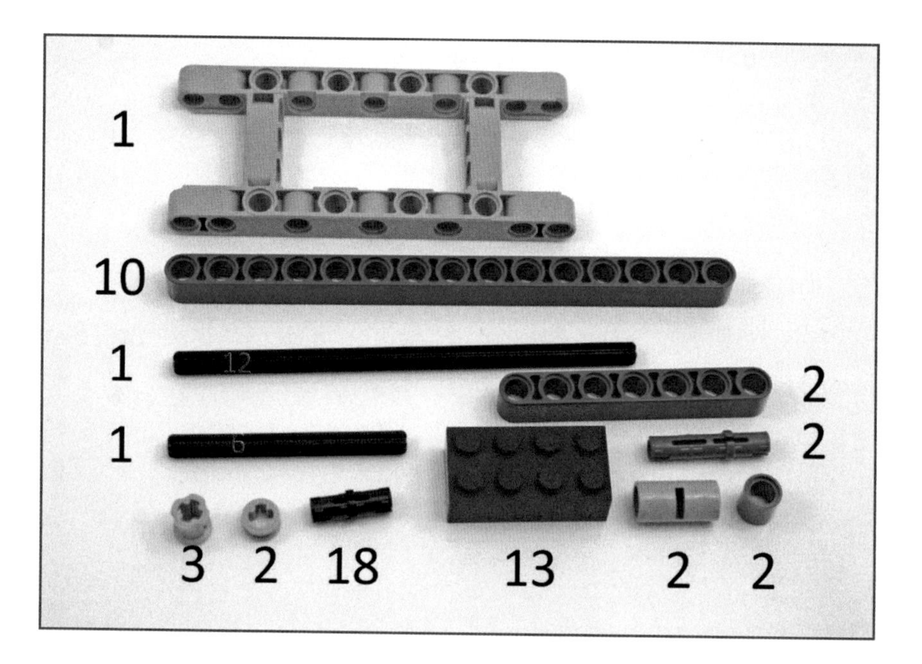


### Procedures:

**Part 1**

1. Build the lever, starting with the fulcrum in the middle, at hole number 19.

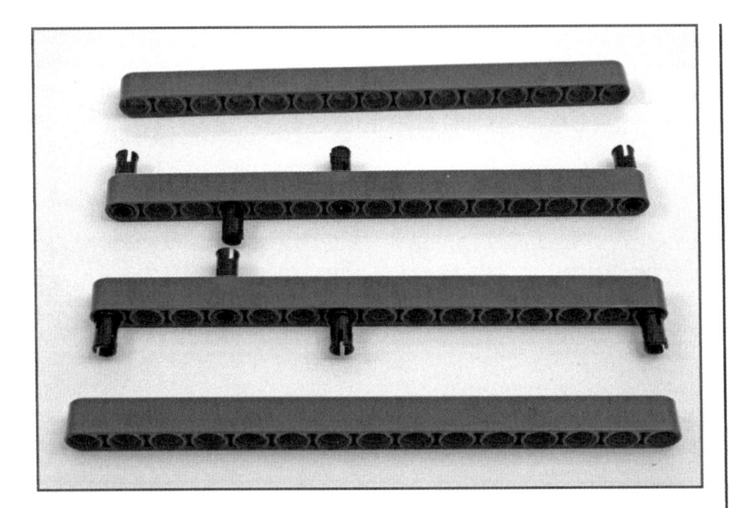

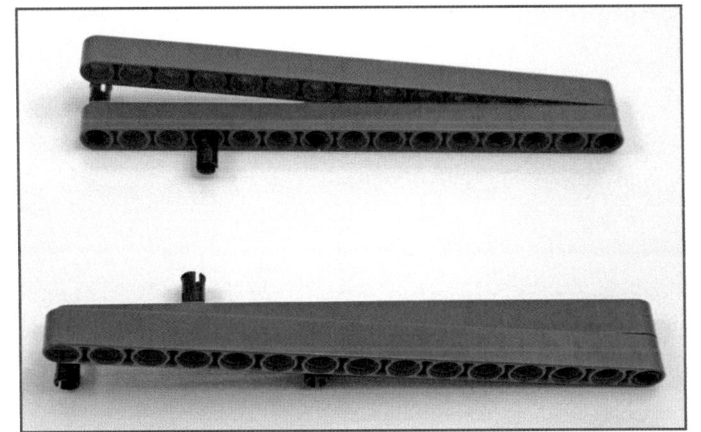

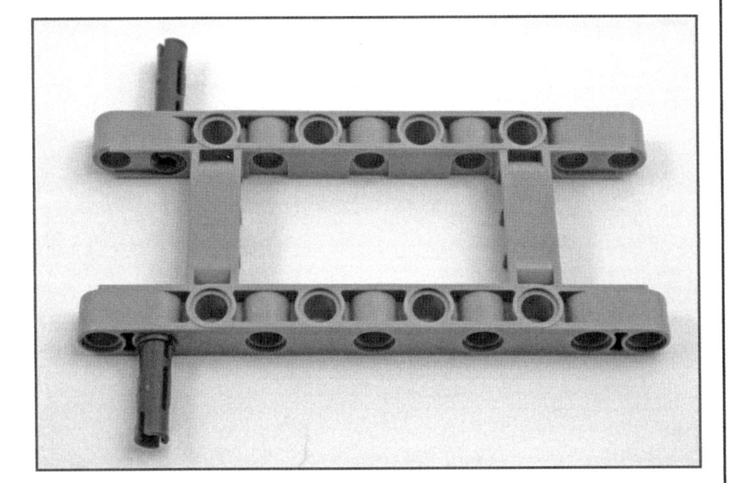

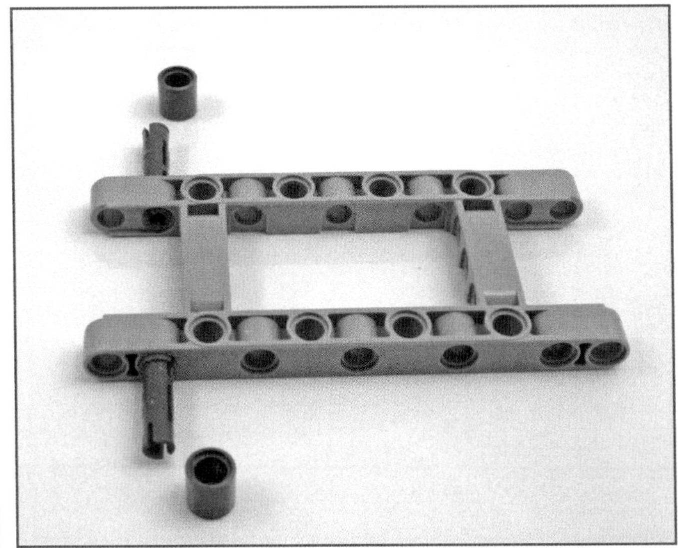

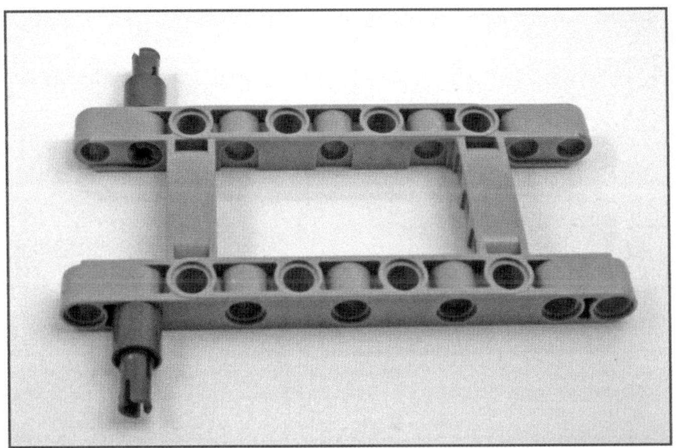

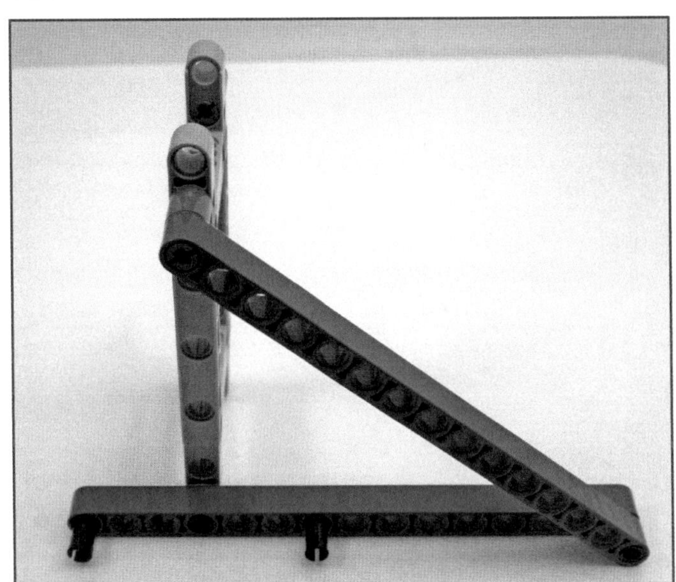

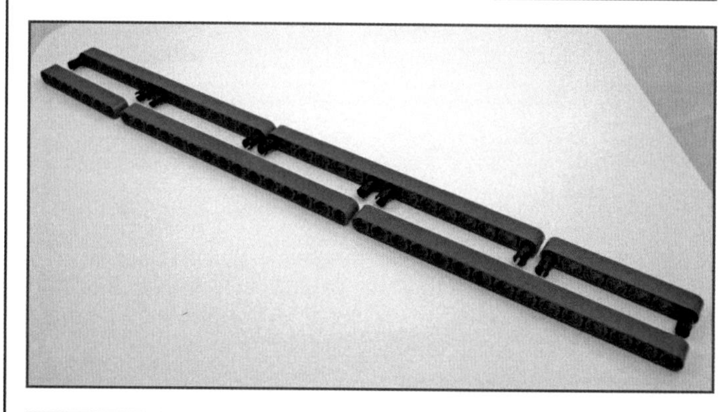

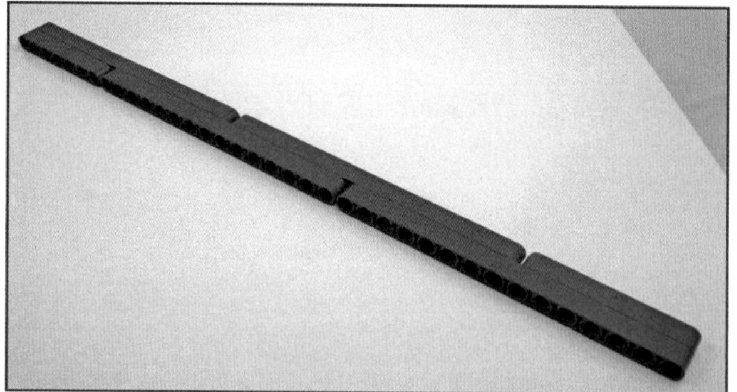

Insert the axle in the middle of the lever.

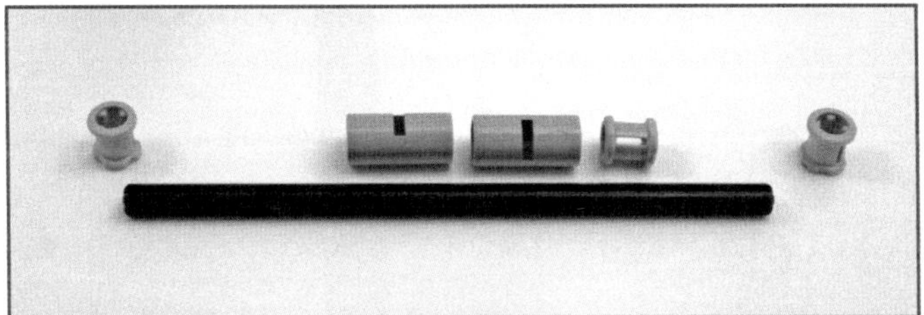

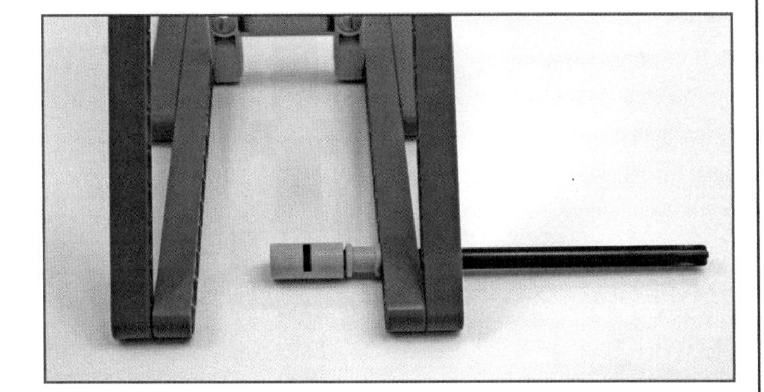

2. Add one 2x4 brick to one side. Note, the bricks can be added by pressing the studs on the top directly into the holes on the lever. The picture helps.

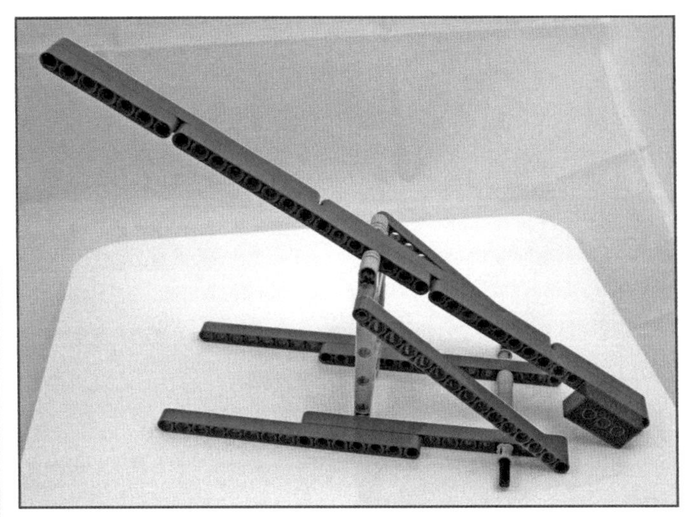

3. Add another brick to the other side, in the mirror image location. That is, the same

distance and location from the fulcrum on both sides. Note that the lever should be balanced.

## Part 2

1. Move the pivot point to the next available hole toward the side with the angled support. A spare axle helps to remove the pivot point axle. We'll be doing this several times, as it's a bit difficult, but you'll get better at it. Note: You don't need to remove the pivot point axle all the way to change positions, just enough to move the lever.

2. Note that the lever is no longer balanced because one side is longer than the other, resulting in it falling toward the long side.
3. Add one 2x4 brick to the short end, as shown, making and recording careful observations.

4. Now add more bricks, for a total of 4 on the short end, balanced on either side of the lever on that short end.

5. Add bricks to the long side until the lever falls to that side again. Note how many bricks it took.

6. Leave what you added to the lever's short side, but remove what was added to the long side.
7. Rearrange the bricks so that you have none on the short side, 4 on the long side, balanced as before, as shown:

8. Add bricks to the short side until the lever moves toward the short side. Record the number of bricks and your observations.

## Part 3

1. Remove all bricks from the lever.
2. Move the pivot point to the next available hole on the short side, at position 14.
3. Add 6 bricks to the short side, balanced on either side of the lever as before. These bricks are the load force that needs to be moved. It might be easier to stack 3 bricks and then add the stack as a whole to the lever.

4. Add bricks to the long side until you move the load force. Note how many it took and record your observations.

**Part 4**

1. Remove all bricks from the lever.
2. Move the fulcrum 2 more holes toward the short side. (This is the last time we'll move it!)
3. Add 10 bricks to the short side, again balanced on either side.
4. Add bricks to the long side until the load is moved. Record your observations.

### Levers Experiment #1: First-Class Levers Discussion

Leverage is greatly increased by the lever's length, and load forces can also be magnified by a lever. You should have noted that it didn't take hardly any effort force (bricks) to move the load force when the load was on the short side. However, when the load was on the long side, it took more effort to move that load. As the pivot point moves and the lever becomes longer, you're able to move a lot of load with little force.

What does this tell us? We can exert a lot of force using a first-class lever. The mechanical advantage may be large, especially when the fulcrum is closer to the load force. Cranes are built either way, with the specific construction depending on its intended purpose. One example is pulling a nail with a pry bar or the claw end of a hammer.

An important consideration that you may have noticed is when a machine has long levers, the lever itself becomes a large factor to consider. In our case, the mass and lever themselves already exerted quite a bit of force depending on the position. In other words, if the lever was vertical, it would exert no force except for gravity, straight down. As it moves toward the horizontal position, more force is exerted at the load force end. These are important considerations for engineers when designing machines. Modeling is required at every position to ensure the machine performs as expected and desired, and will do so safely.

## Levers Experiment #2: Second-Class Levers

Remember: the load force is between the fulcrum and the effort force in second-class levers. Examples are a wheelbarrow or a wrench.

### Parts Needed:

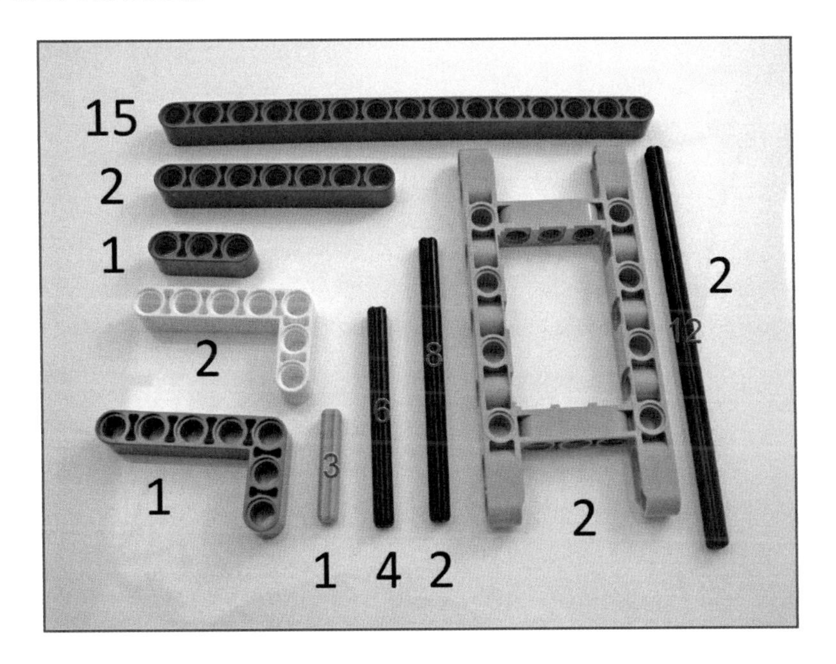


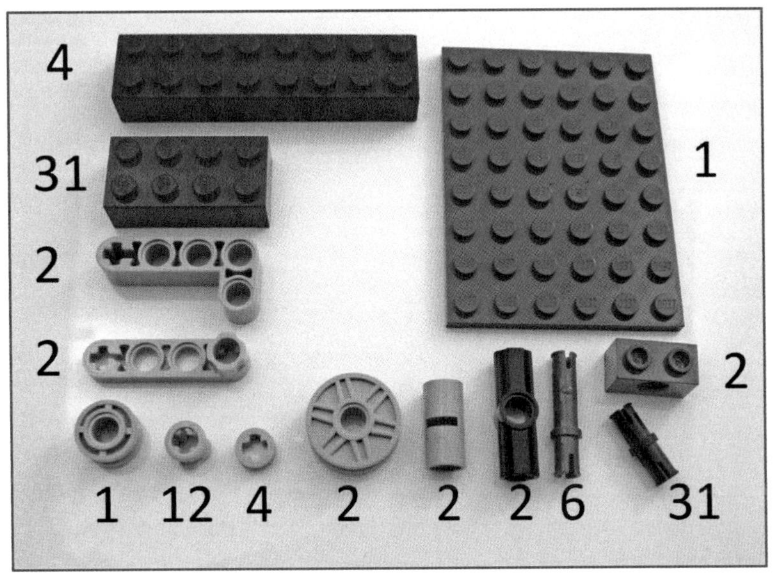

**Procedures:**

1. Build the tower and lever.

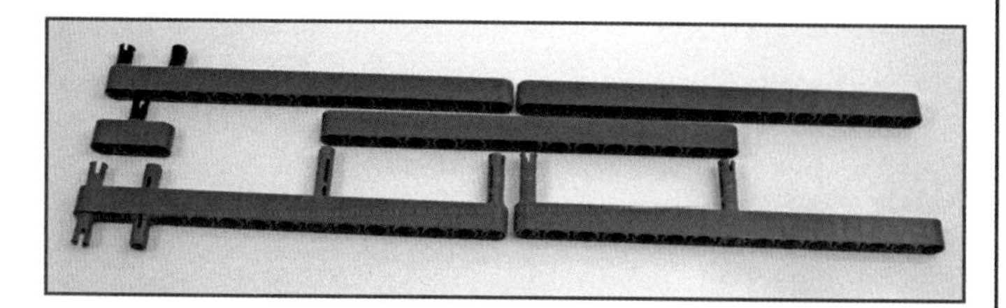

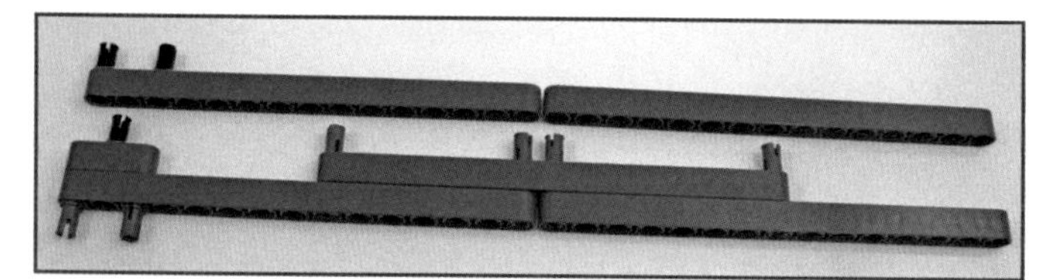

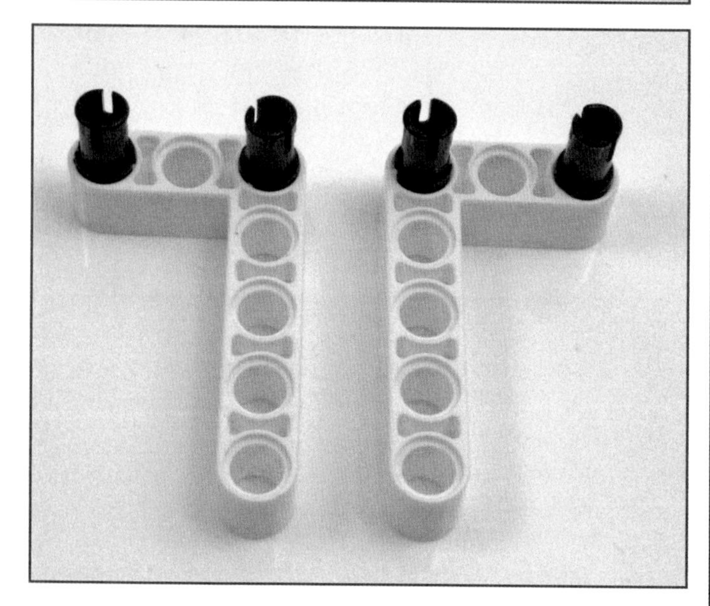

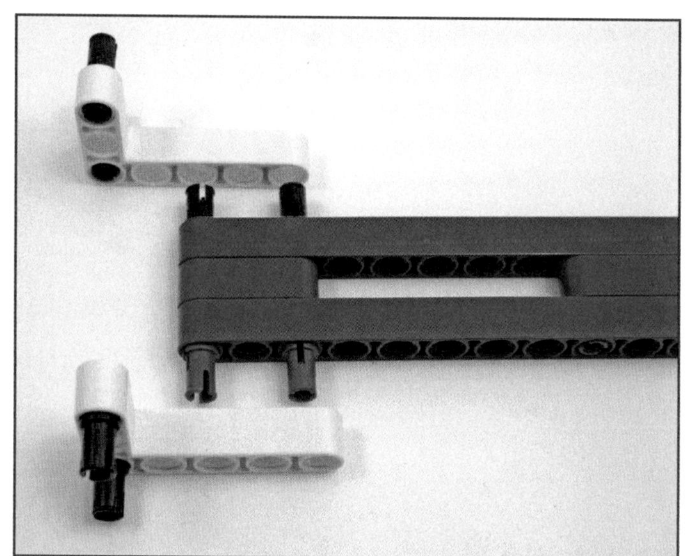

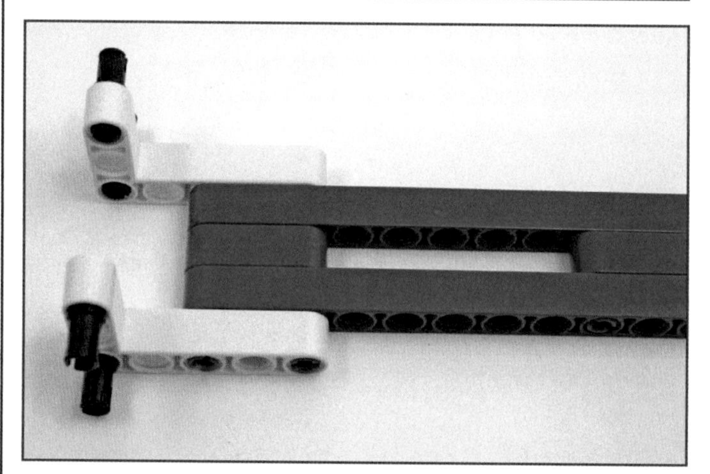

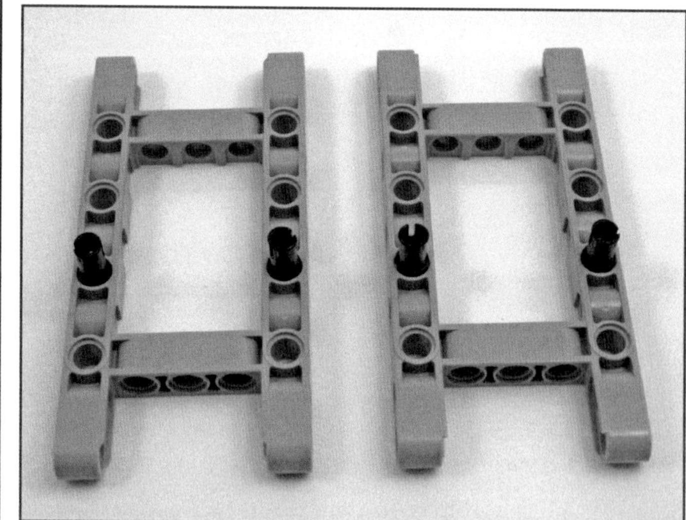

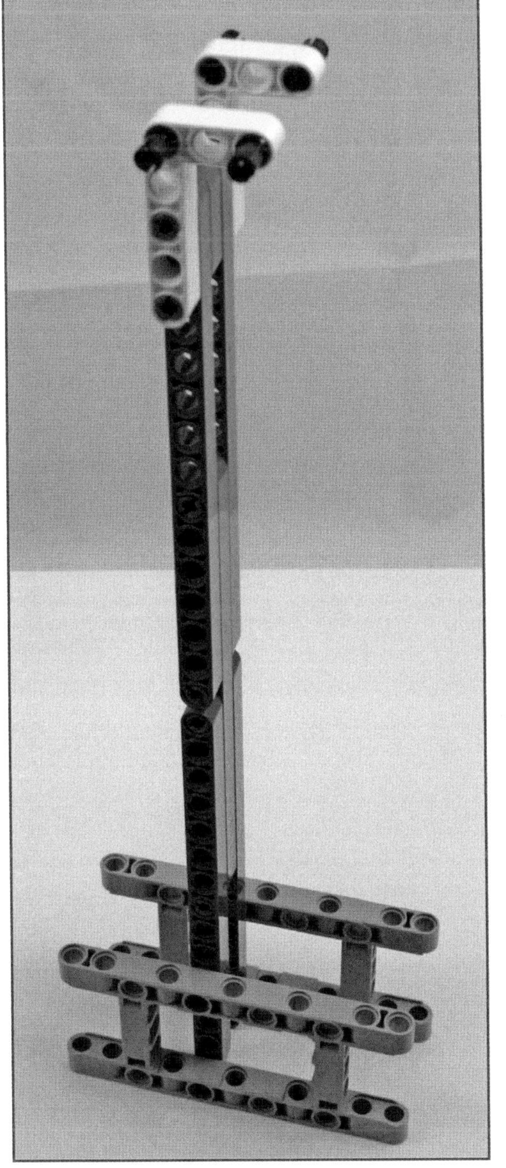

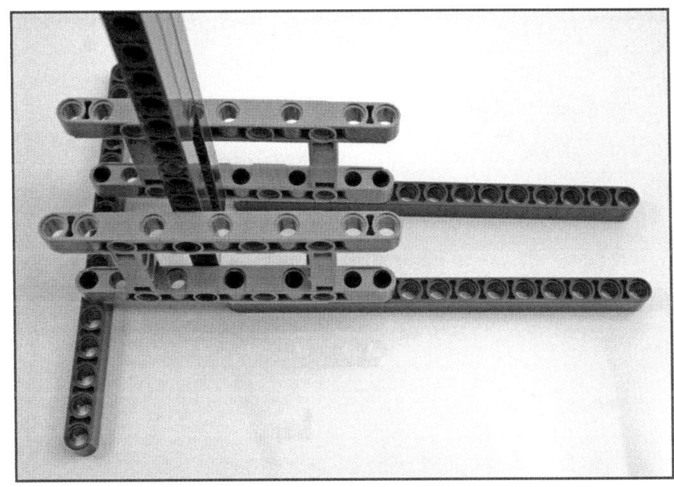

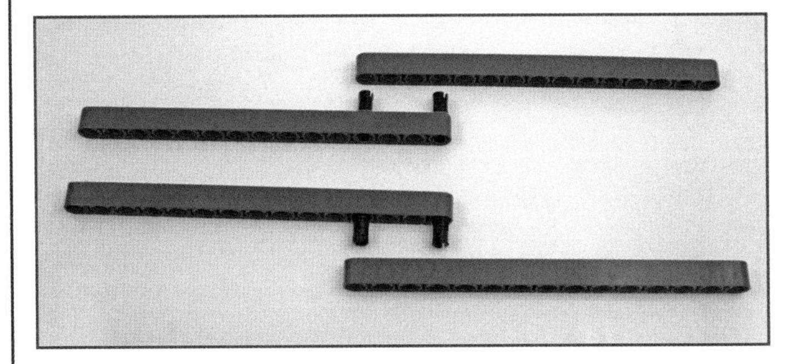

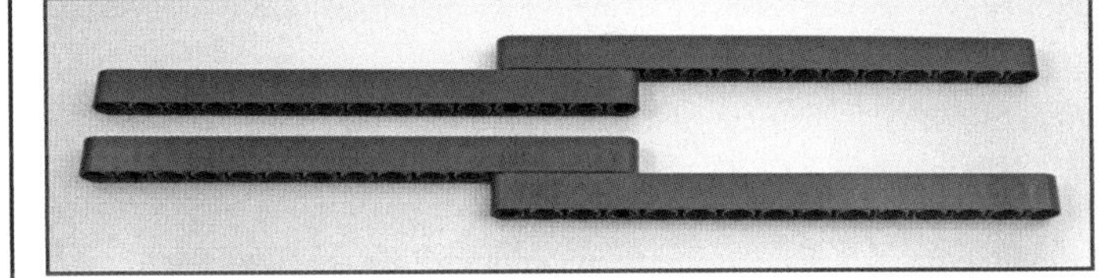

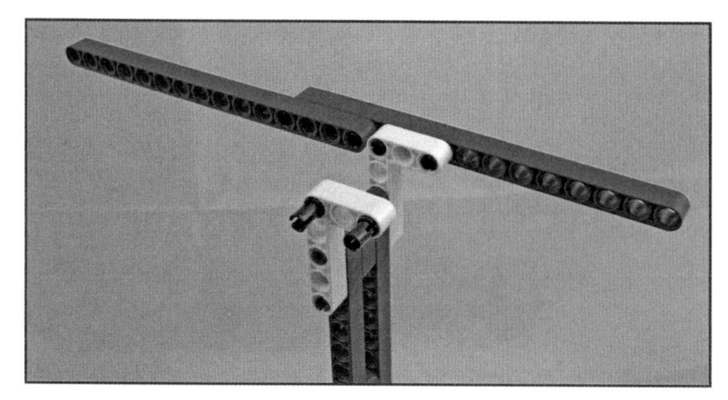

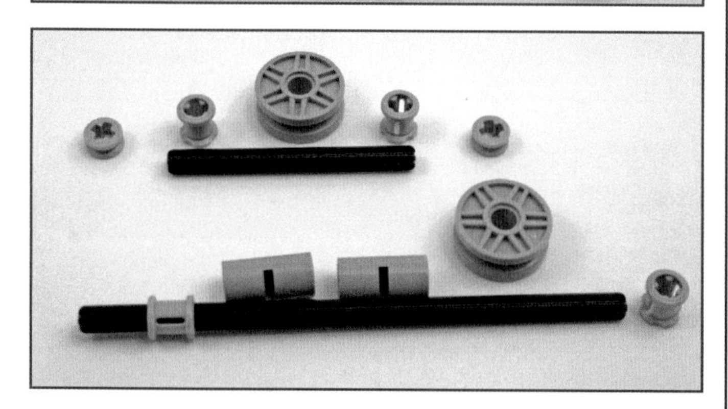

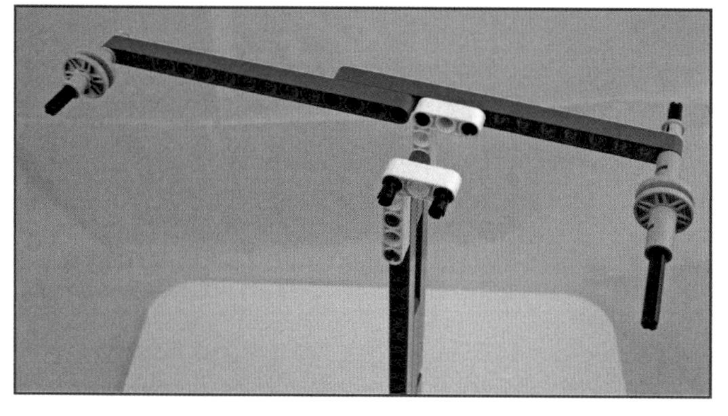

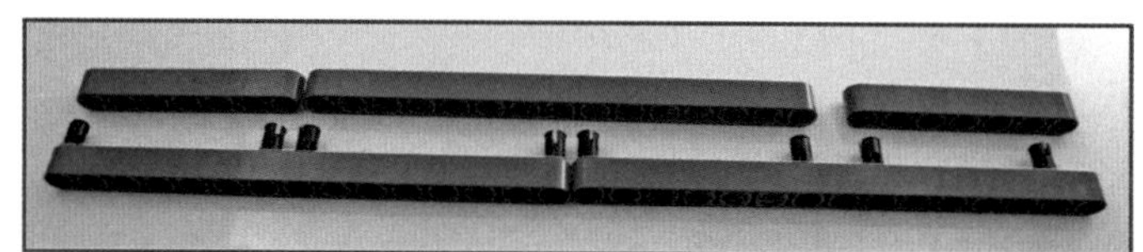

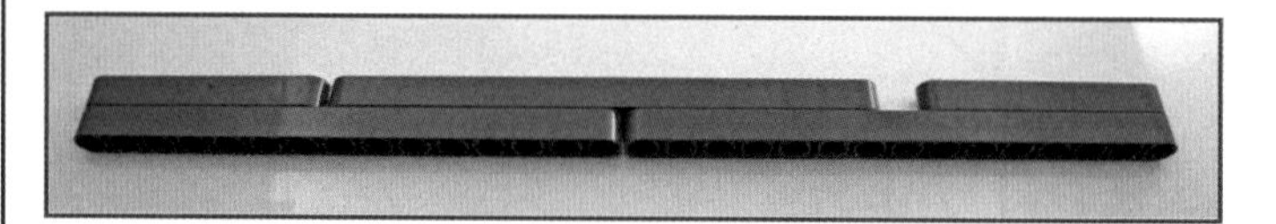

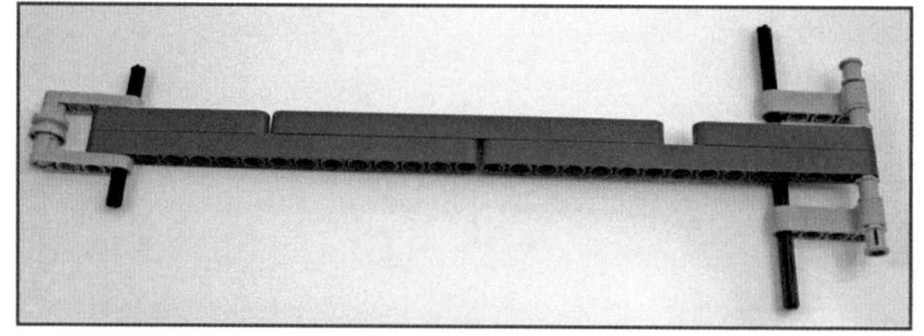

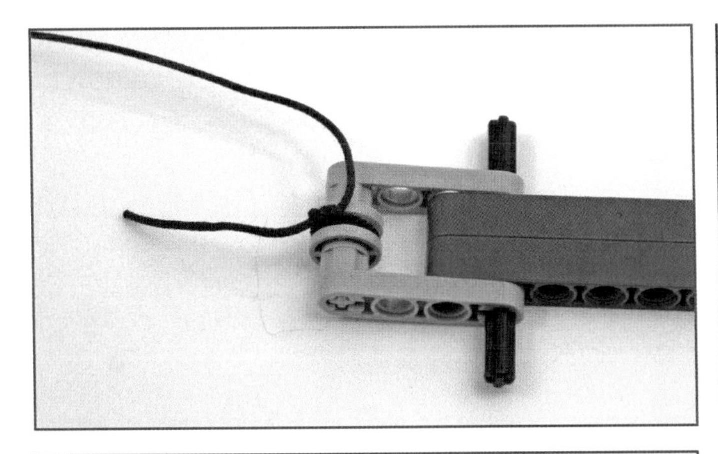

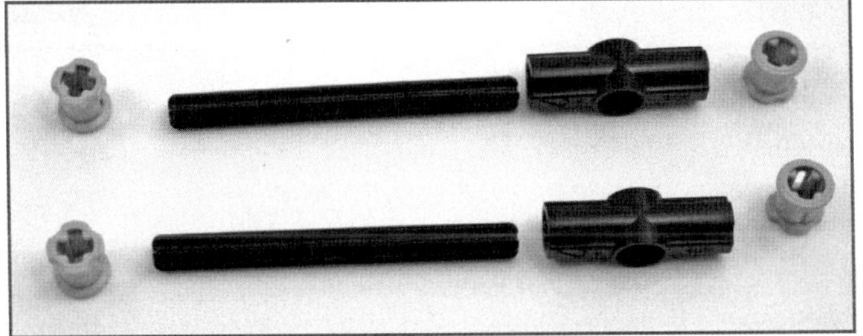

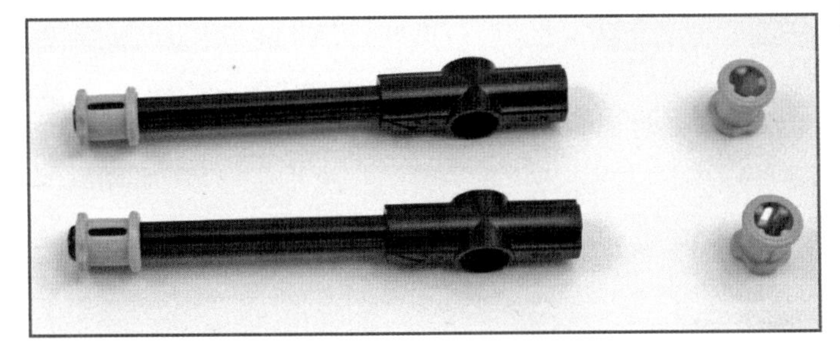

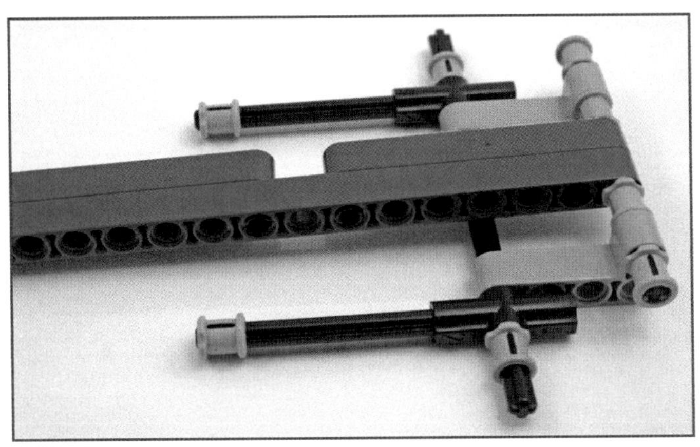

2. Make sure the rigging (referring to the string) moves freely and is in the proper grooves. For best results, the model should be on a smooth surface, such as a tabletop.

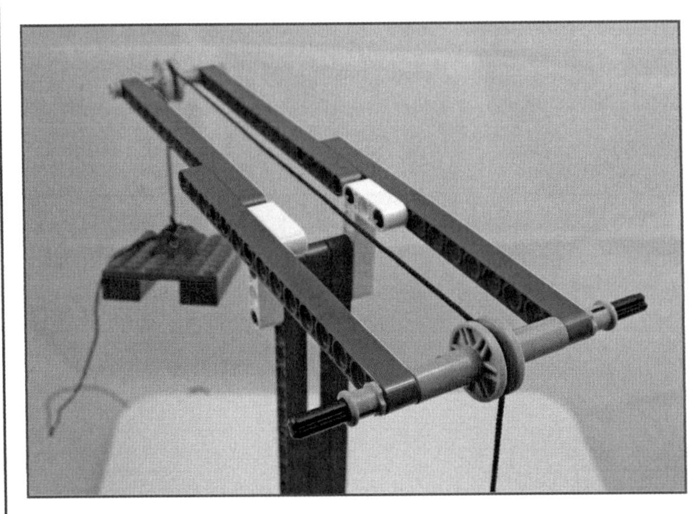

3. Place ten 2x4 bricks as a load force.

4. Add 2x4 bricks to the counterweight as the effort force until the lever lifts, and note the number of bricks needed.

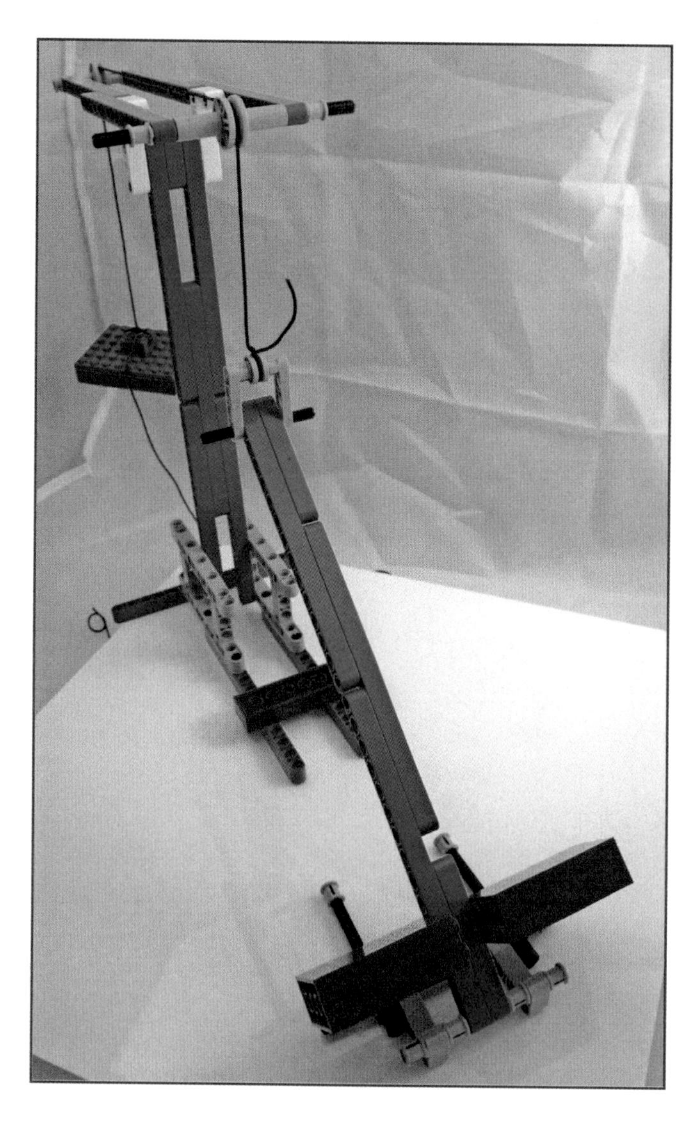

5. Move the weight (load force) toward the lever's load force end, about halfway up the lever. The lever will fall.

6. Add more 2x4 bricks to the counterweight until the lever lifts again.

7. Move the weight one more time, near the effort force end of the lever, as shown. Add more 2x4 bricks to the counterweight until the lever lifts again. Record the number of bricks required and your observations.

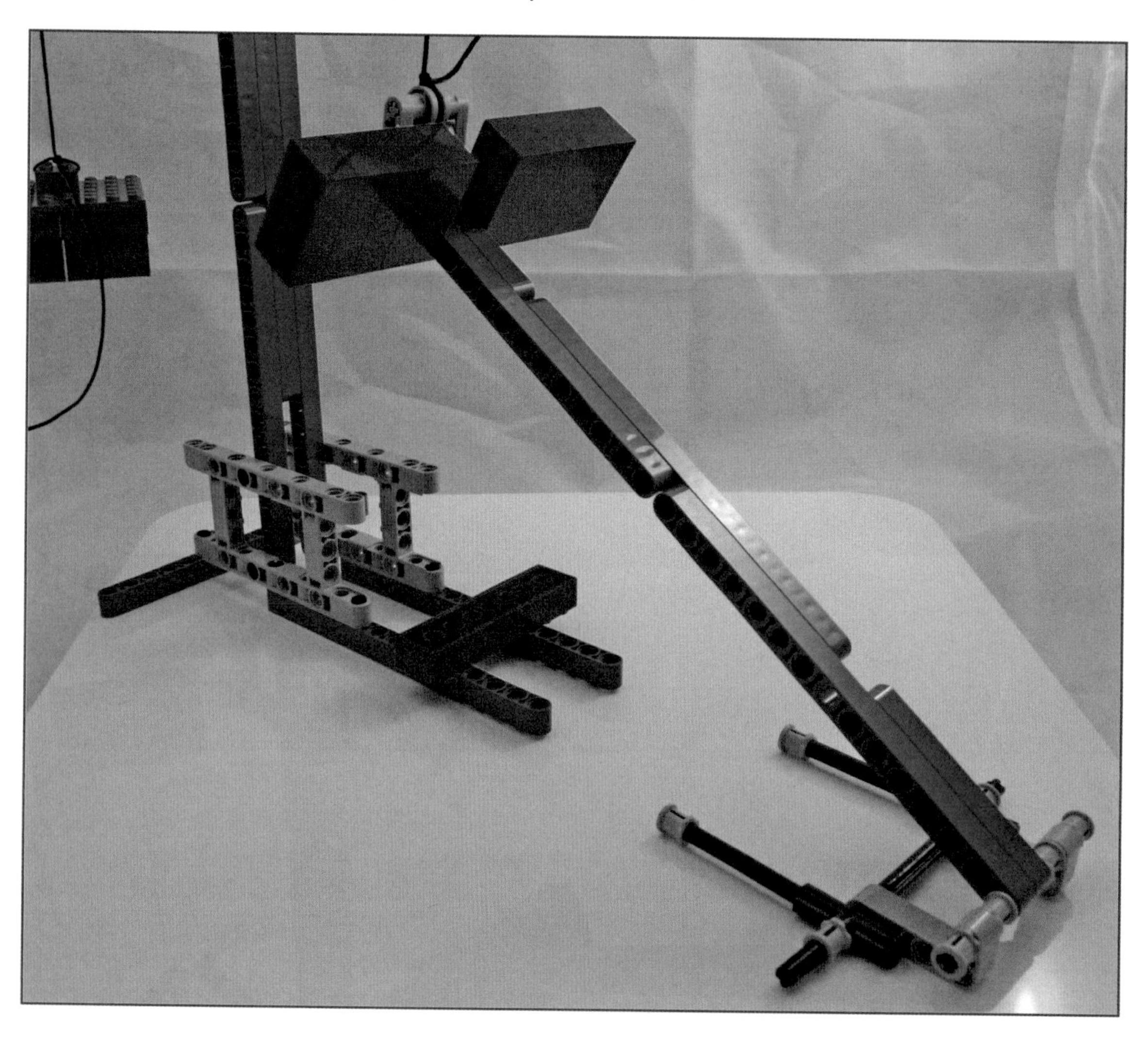

### Levers Experiment #2: Second-Class Levers Discussion

Based on these results, if you have to move things in a wheelbarrow, where would you want the heaviest objects? Toward the handles or closer to the wheel? The answer is, "It depends." Most likely you'd want them closer to the wheel, as it would make them easier to lift. However, it can also make the load less stable. The closer it is to the handles, the more the load can be stabilized since the handles are far apart. The wheelbarrow operator's strength and skill, and terrain roughness, are some of the many variables involved when using this machine.

You may have noticed again evidence of Newton's first law. It takes a bit of energy to get something moving, but once it starts, it moves more easily with as much energy as it took to get it moving…as long as you don't run into rough terrain, an increasing incline, or other variable changes. Inertia is one reason why experiments such as this don't always turn out exactly the same. In order to have more repeatability, all other variables would need to be controlled, including temperature, humidity, the exact string placement, surface roughness from location to location, etc. For our purposes, recognizing that these things do play a part is sufficient.

*Note: If you're moving on to Levers Experiment #3: Third-Class Levers, don't take apart the tower since it's needed for that experiment.*

## Levers Experiment #3: Third-Class Levers

Remember: third-class levers have the effort force between the fulcrum and the load force. Examples include tweezers and the action of the bicep on your forearm.

### Parts Needed (In addition to parts from Experiment #2):

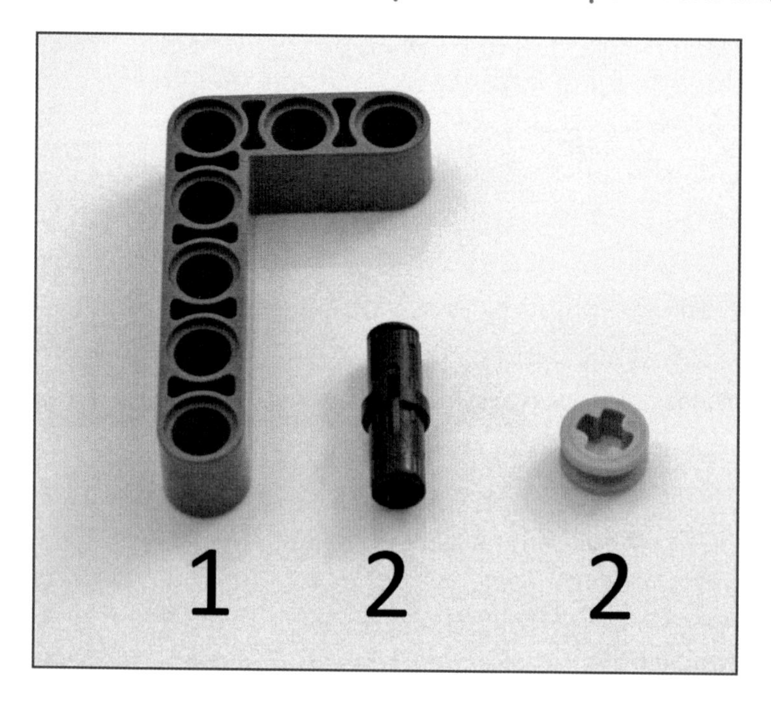


### Procedures

1. Build the tower. Refer to instructions from levers Experiment #2, or use the same tower, with slight modifications as shown:

2. Build the third-class lever assembly. The lever itself is the same as for Experiment #2.

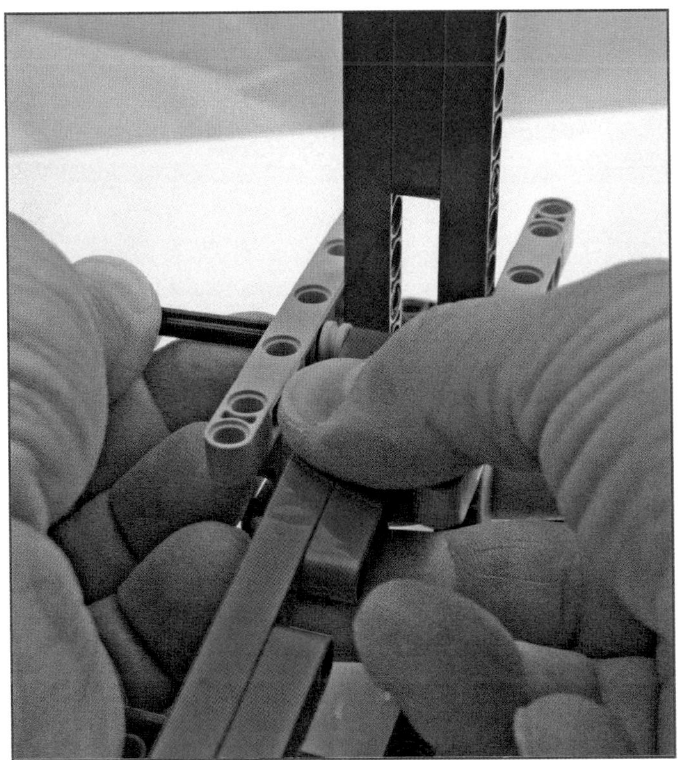

3. Reattach the string with the lever down and the counterweight at the top of the tower. Make sure the rigging runs smoothly in the proper channels, with no binding in parts that should move.
4. Attach the effort force rigging to hole #9 from the load force end. Attach 6 bricks on either side of the load end, as shown. The finished assembly should look like this:

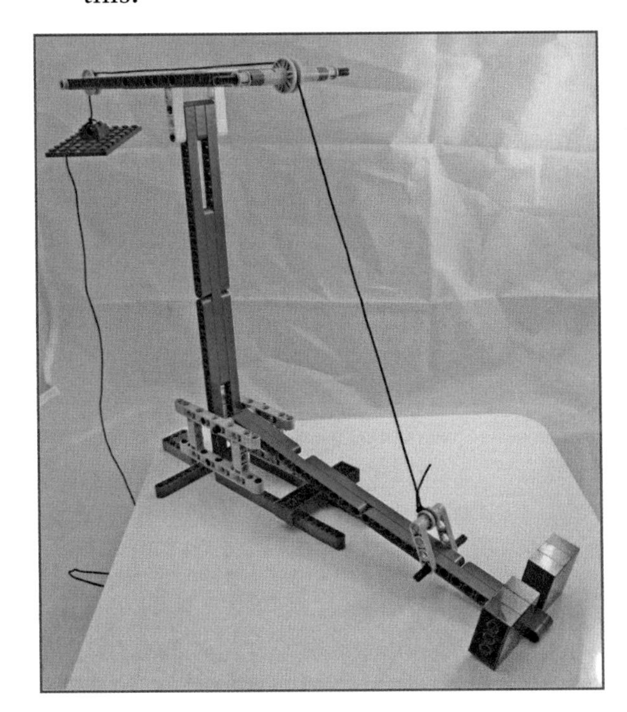

5. Now attach bricks to the counterweight. How many bricks have to be attached to the counterweight to begin to lift the lever?

6. Move the effort force application point to 14 holes from the load end. Note again the number of bricks it takes to lift the lever.

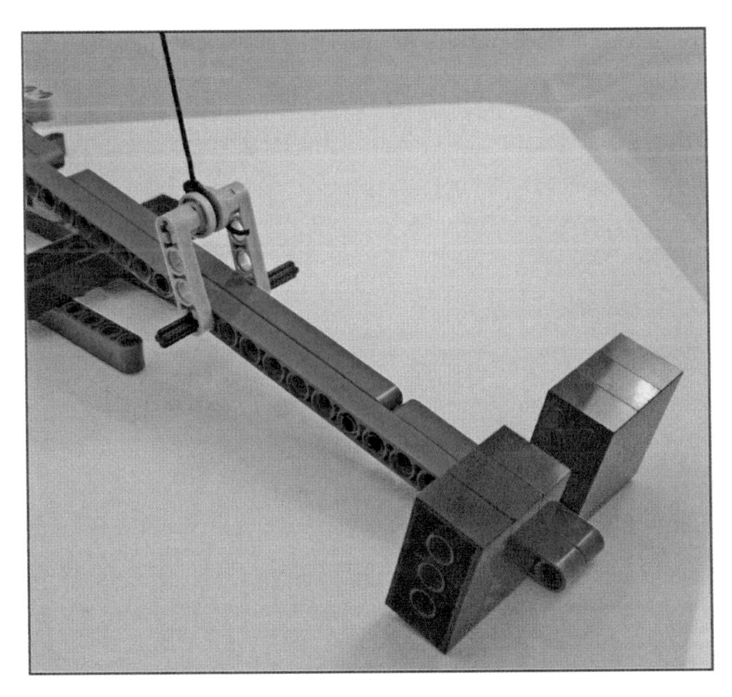

7. How many bricks are needed on the effort end to lift the load? Note any observations to this point.

8. Move the attachment point for the effort force one more time, to 21 holes from the load force end. How many bricks does it take to raise the lever this time? Note: You might have to even remove a brick or 2 from the load end in order to get the lever to lift. Record your observations. You can experiment with other available holes.

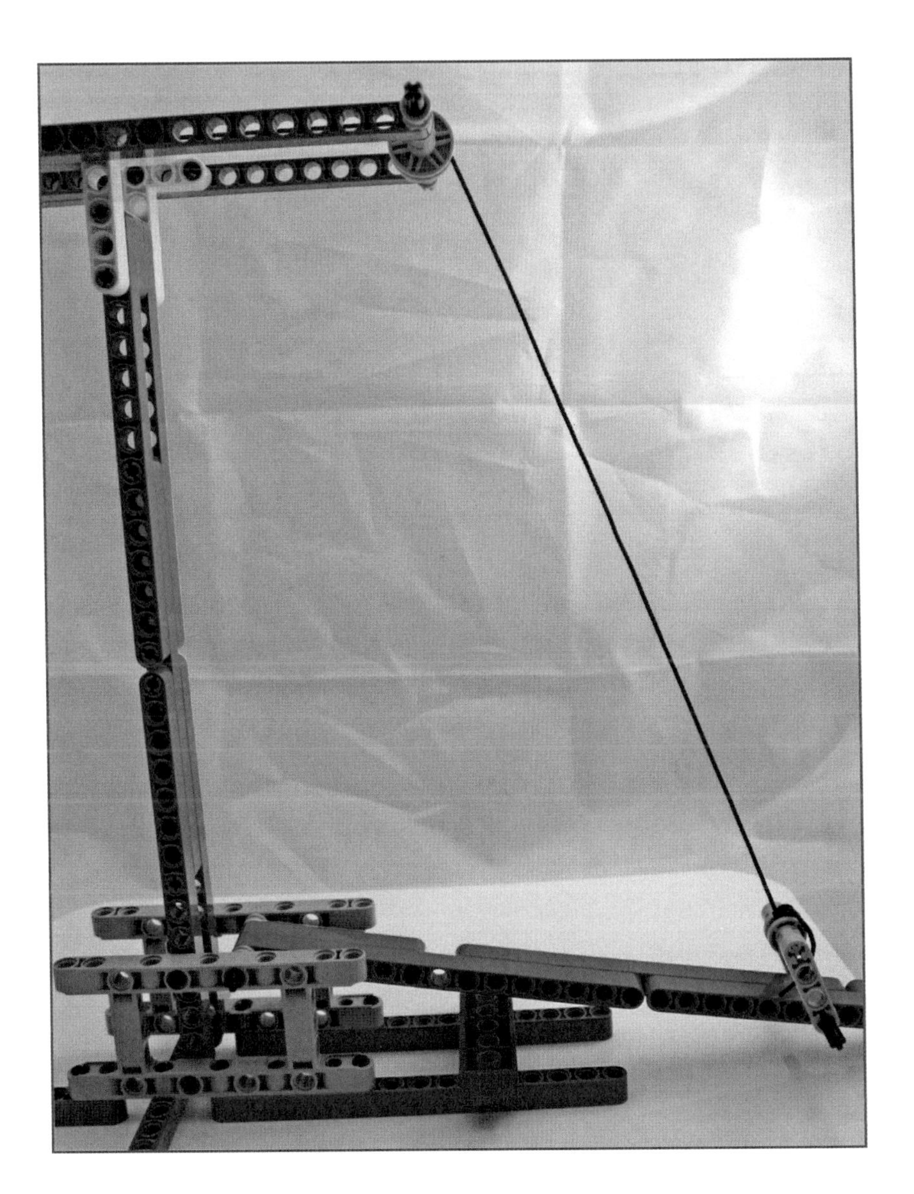

9. Try moving the string off the blocks or pulleys once you've found the amount of bricks that make the load rise. What happened? Can you explain it?

### Levers Experiment #3: Third-Class Levers Discussion

As previously mentioned, the fact that third-class levers are widely used is strange. They have no mechanical advantage; in fact, in the last experiment, it took a lot of bricks to lift a light load! The reason they are so prevalent is because of the extended reach they provide.

When designing these levers, current mathematical understanding allows for exact, realistic computer modeling to determine the most efficient placement of effort force attachment, pivot, and load force points. Usually a specific need, or set of needs, is identified first, and then a machine is designed and engineered to fulfill the need most efficiently. You may have noticed that when the strings were moved off the pulleys, it took more bricks to raise the lever. It's possible the lever didn't come up at all. The reason is increased friction of the rigging (string) on the tower.

Did you notice that sometimes the lever will lift a little, then stop? Or, depending on the attachment point of the effort force, sometimes the lever would slowly start to lift, then accelerate. Why do you suppose this happens? The primary reason is the angle to which the force is applied changes as the lever rises, altering the amount of force that's actually applied to the object. As angles continue to move, the amount of force needed must be modified to maintain the same speed.

## WHAT DO YOU THINK?

**See what else you can make! The process of taking proven principles and converting them into useful machines is basic to engineering. That means you're engineering! It's fascinating to go back and look at old machinery books written before electric motors, servos, etc. were available. The complicated machinery designed and constructed to move power around is truly ingenious, and the machines accomplished a great variety of work.**

## JOURNALING IDEA

If you were designing a new kind of animal, how would you incorporate different types of levers into its muscular skeletal system? Try drawing some pictures of muscles on the skeleton, including where they attach, to provide the movement you want for your new animal.

## CHAPTER REVIEW

1. Move the joints in your body and try to identify what type of lever it is. You'll be surprised at how many of your joints are third-class levers! For example, the bicep muscle (effort force) attaches to the forearm bone between the fulcrum (the elbow joint) and the load force (whatever is in your hand you're trying to lift). It's a third-class lever! If you aren't sure, take a look at an anatomy book and examine where the muscles attach to the bone.

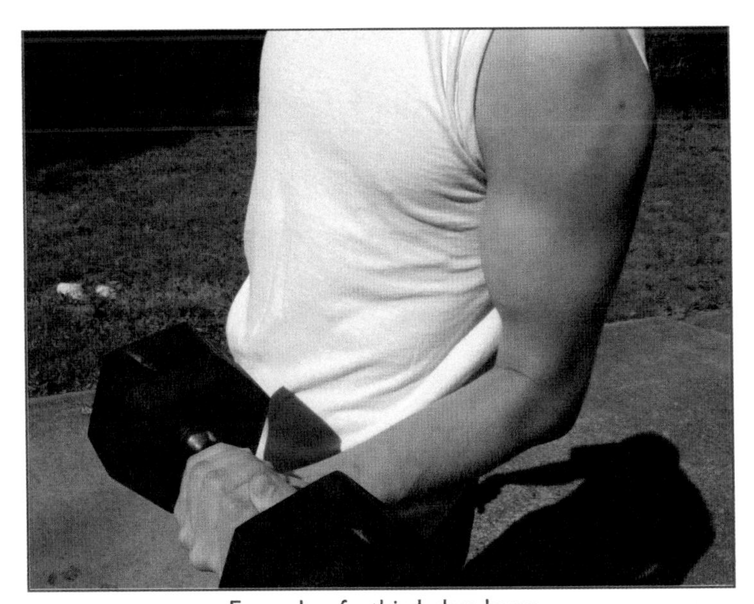

Example of a third-class lever

2. Identify as many types of levers as you can in the yellow backhoe and front loader photo. How about the white and blue crane in the background?

Backhoe and crane[21]

3. Think of a task around you that you either do or are asked to do on a frequent basis. See if you can think of a lever-based design for a tool or machine that can help with the job.
4. Go through your kitchen, identifying and listing all the utensils that are levers, including what type of lever.

| Description | Lever type |
|---|---|
| | |
| | |
| | |
| | |
| | |
| | |
| | |

5. Lastly, look at the list of utensils from your kitchen. Describe in your own words what food preparation would be like without them. If you don't have a lot of food preparation experience, ask someone in your household who does. For example, you could take tongs (a third-class lever) and describe how it would be to live as if they'd never been invented.

# CHAPTER 3

# SIMPLE MACHINES: THE INCLINED PLANE

## HISTORY

The inclined plane is an ancient simple machine that reduces the force needed to move something vertically.

The Great Mosque of Samarra[22]

Building a pyramid[23]

Recognizing the increased effort needed to move the same load up a hill, ancient people even noted an increased cost schedule. It took more horses to move a load up a steep *grade* than across a level grade.

Think of this the next time you pass a large truck struggling up a steep road!

***Grade:*** A term describing the degree of inclination of a road. You will often see it expressed in percentage. For example, a 12 percent grade is steeper than an 8 percent grade.

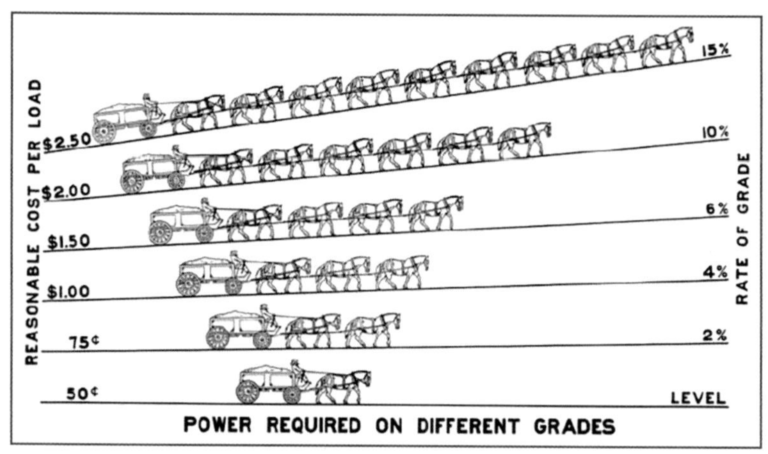


An old cost schedule for different grades[24]

## INCLINED PLANES

The greatest effort required to move an object is straight up. Since we're familiar with Newton's laws, we know the effort force will be greater than the load force. If we want to reduce the effort force, we can reduce the angle and push or pull the object. Depending on the friction between an object and the surface it's resting on, the result can be a greatly reduced effort force required. The object can be transferred more safely as well since it isn't swinging in the air. Many methods have been devised to pull objects up an incline. Before the advent of electric motors, there were some ingenious methods for moving things. There still are, of course. Let's hope we remember them if the power ever goes out for a while!

***Parbuckling:*** A method for rolling a cylindrical object up an incline by running a rope or cable under an object and back up the incline, where it's then pulled, combining a wheel and axle and an inclined plane into a complex machine.

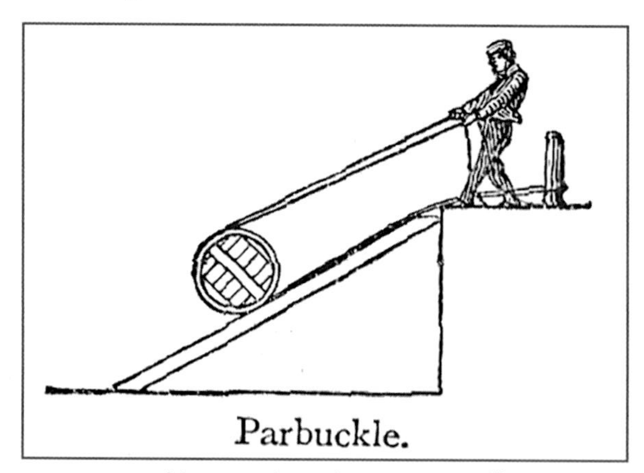


Moving a barrel up an incline[25]

**Parbuckling rig:**
https://www.youtube.com/watch?v=f0T9dz-IvMY

An inclined plane:

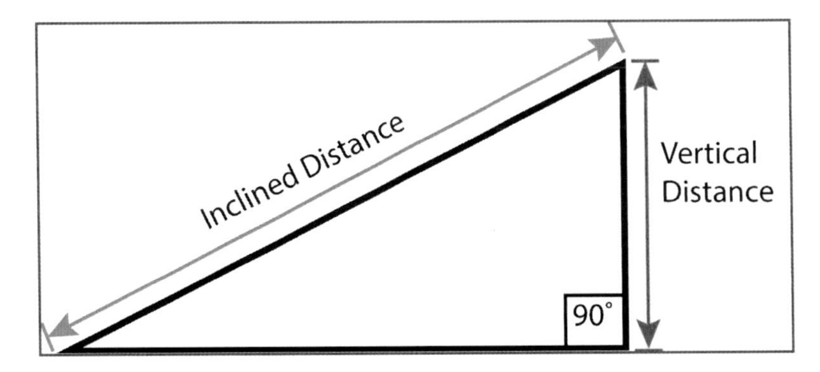


The mechanical advantage of an inclined plane can be calculated:

> *Mechanical advantage = inclined distance ÷ vertical distance*

We know that *Work = force x distance*. For an inclined plane, the longer the distance traveled—accomplished by decreasing the *pitch*, or grade, of the inclined plane—the less force needed to move an object the vertical distance. However, you do have to exert that reduced force for a longer distance. Why would you do that? One reason might be if a required larger force isn't available to move the object the vertical distance. For example, you might not be physically capable of moving a 50 lb. bundle of shingles onto a roof. However, if you angle a ladder against the house side and slide the shingles up the ladder, it's possible because it takes less effort.

## Wedge

A specialized version of an inclined plane is putting two together, with the inclined sides out. This results in a wedge:

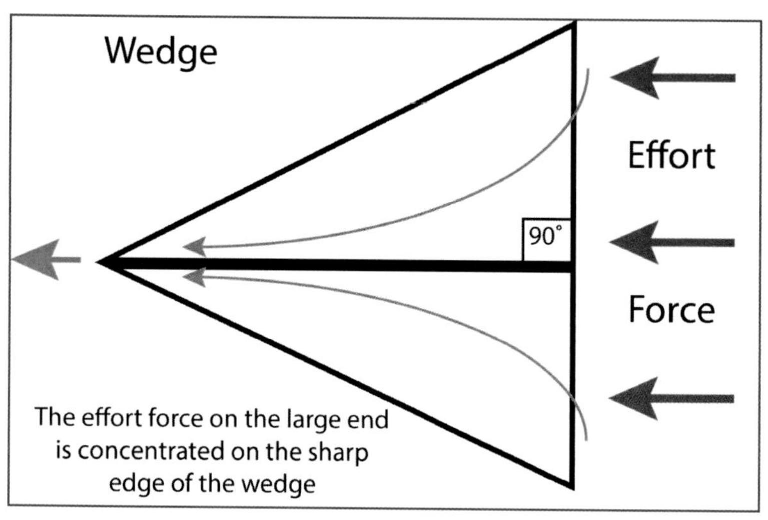


Wedge illustration

A large force can be easily and safely applied to the flat side of the wedge. The force is concentrated on the sharp end, allowing it to be driven into something more easily.

Let's look at a couple examples. First, cutting cheese with a knife. A knife has a sharp edge and an opposite edge that's wider. The result is a wedge with a handle. Force can be applied to the handle or the wide edge of the knife. This force is then concentrated on the knife edge, allowing for easy and controlled cutting action.

Another example: imagine trying to split a log with a sledgehammer. Whacking logs with a sledgehammer certainly warms you up, but you're not likely to get a lot of splitting accomplished! Instead, use an axe. Like a knife, an axe is a wedge on a handle. However, in the case of an axe, rather than pushing on the wide side, force is applied by swinging the handle and hitting the wood with the knife edge. Axes work quite well at splitting wood!

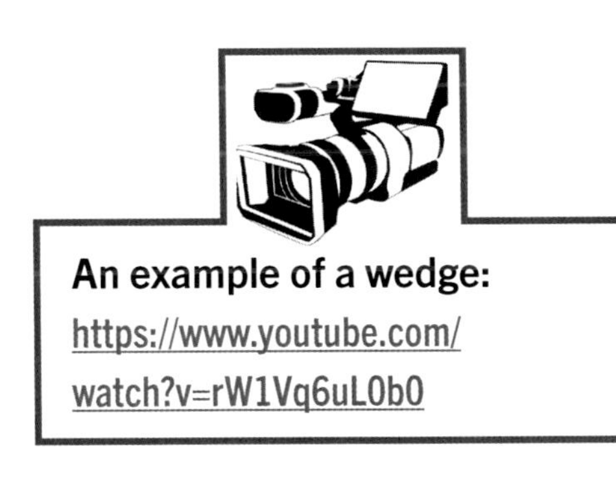

**An example of a wedge:**
https://www.youtube.com/watch?v=rW1Vq6uL0b0

Other common examples of wedges include forks, cheese graters, vegetable peelers, metal nails, and push pins. Anything with a sharp point or a knife edge that widens to a larger width where force can be applied is making use of wedge physics.

## Screw

Another version of an inclined plane is a screw, which is an inclined plane wrapped around a shaft. It can also be thought of as a wedge wrapped around a shaft. In this case, as force is applied, the object "pulled" up the incline is the material into which the screw is being driven. For example, a screw being driven into wood pulls up the wood and makes the screw sink down correspondingly.

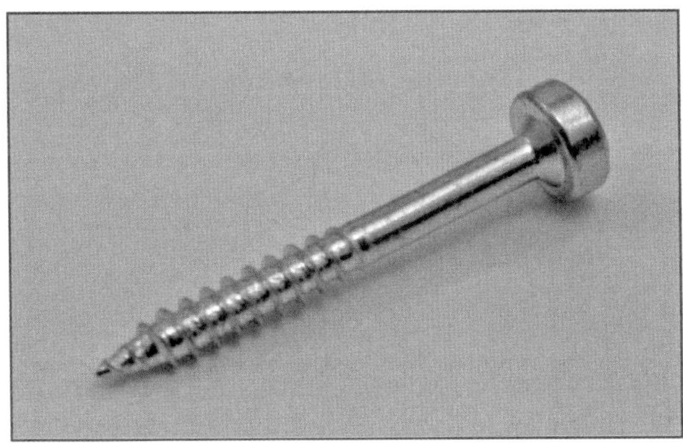

A screw

## EXPERIMENTS: LET'S BUILD SOMETHING!

### Inclined Plane Experiments #1: Angles

Exciting stuff! You get to experience firsthand the effect an increased angle, or reduced mechanical advantage, has on the effort to move an object up an incline.

### Parts Needed:

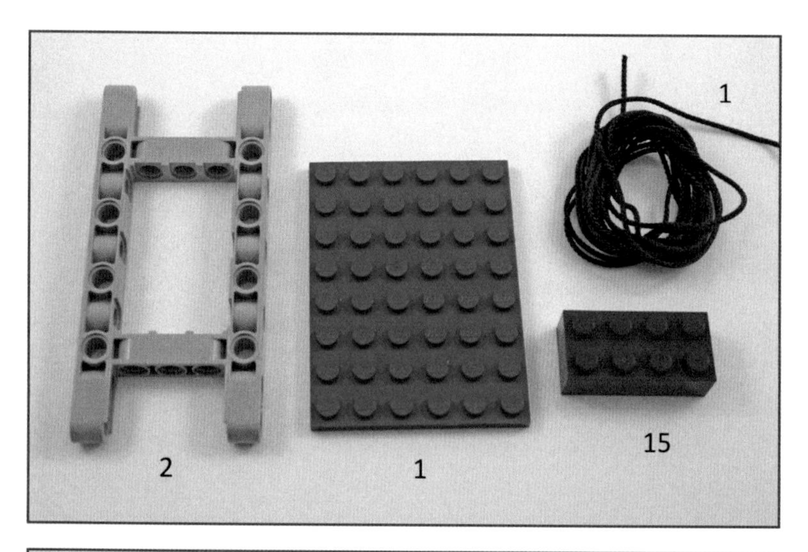


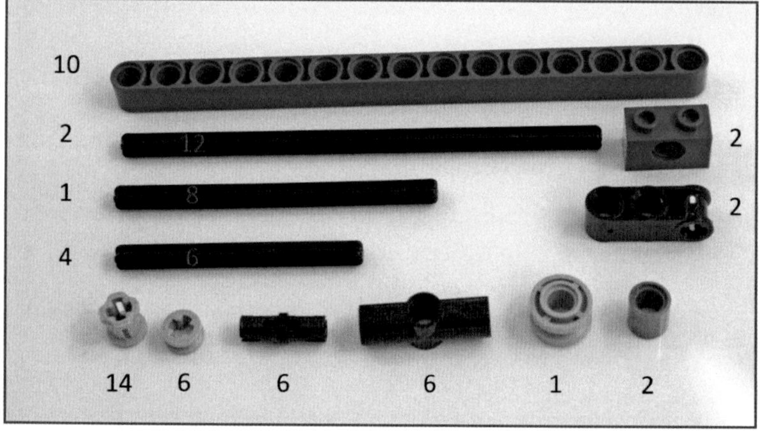

## Procedures

### Angle 1

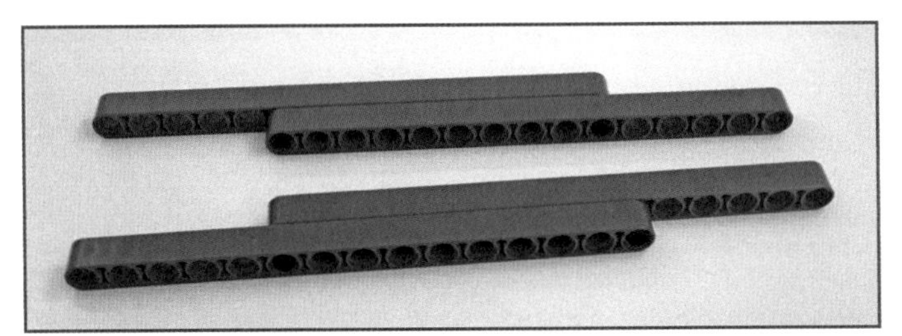

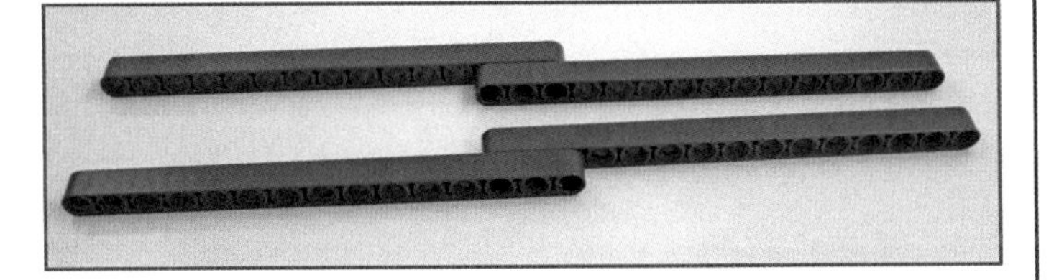

1. Build the angle tower.

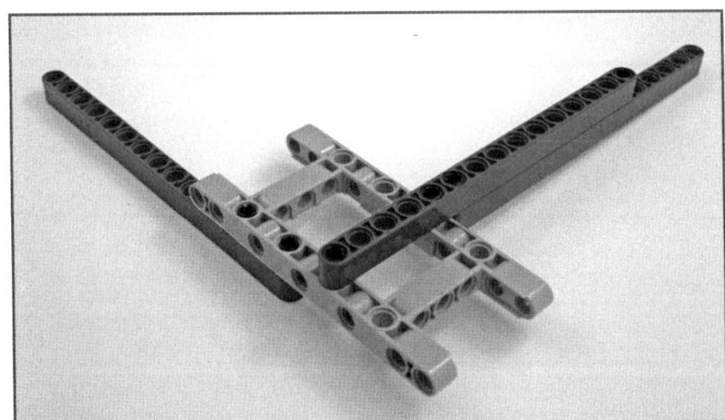

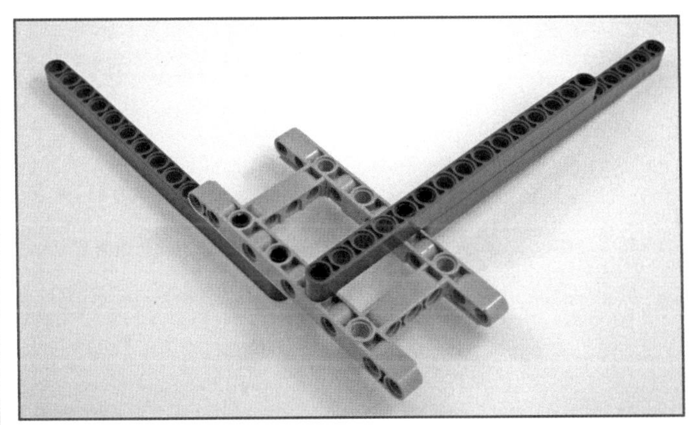

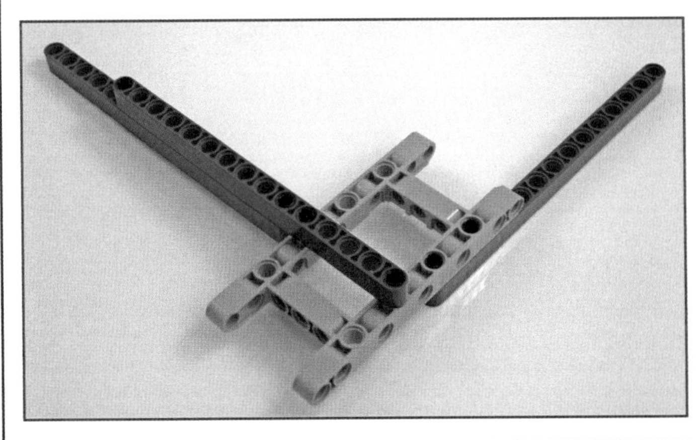

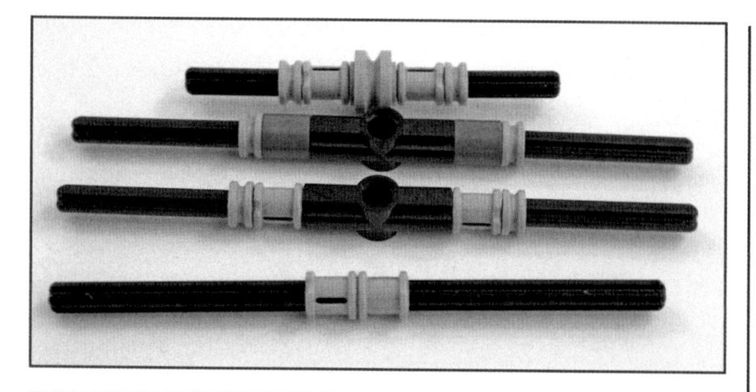

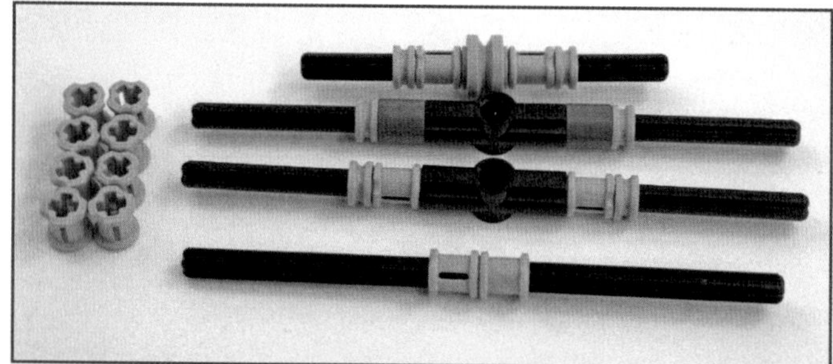

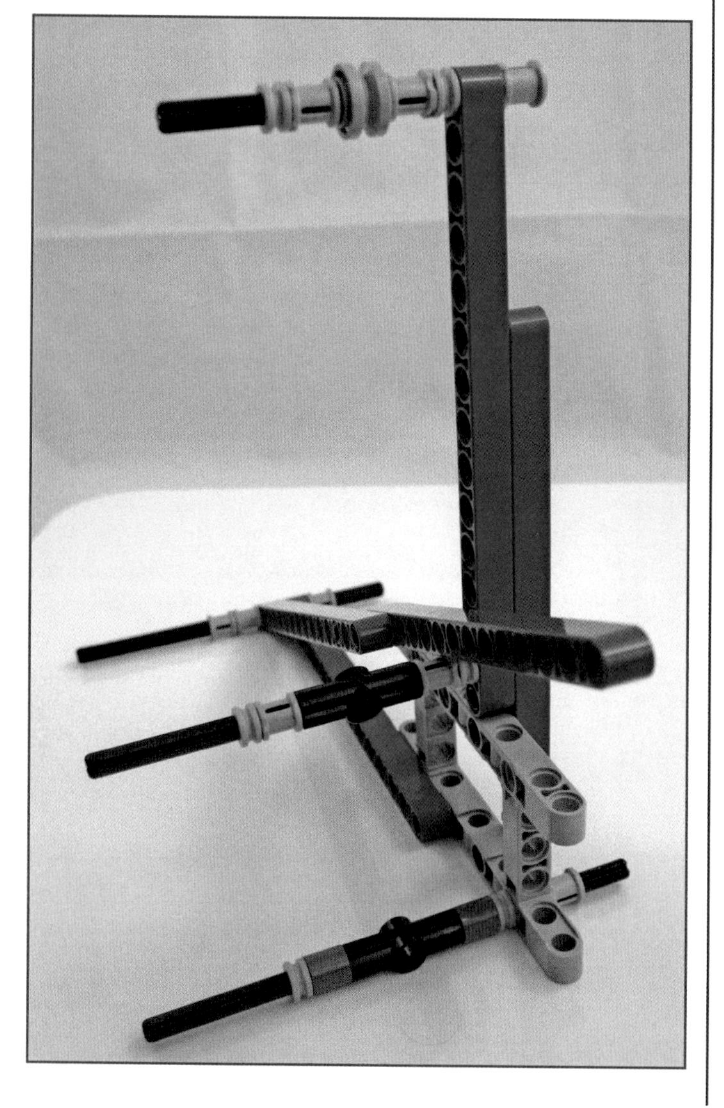

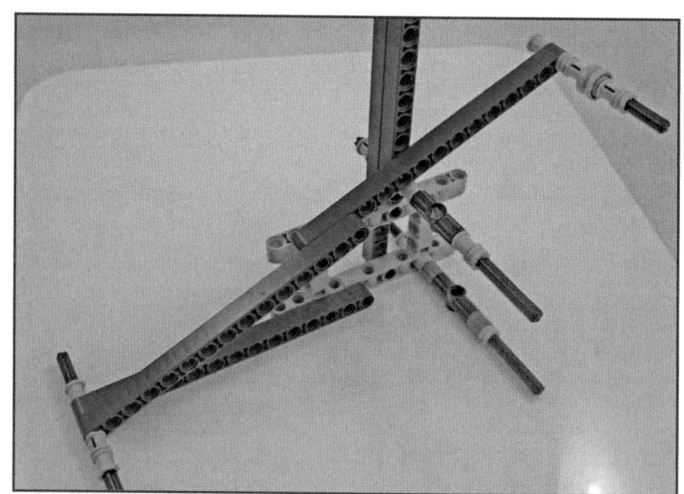

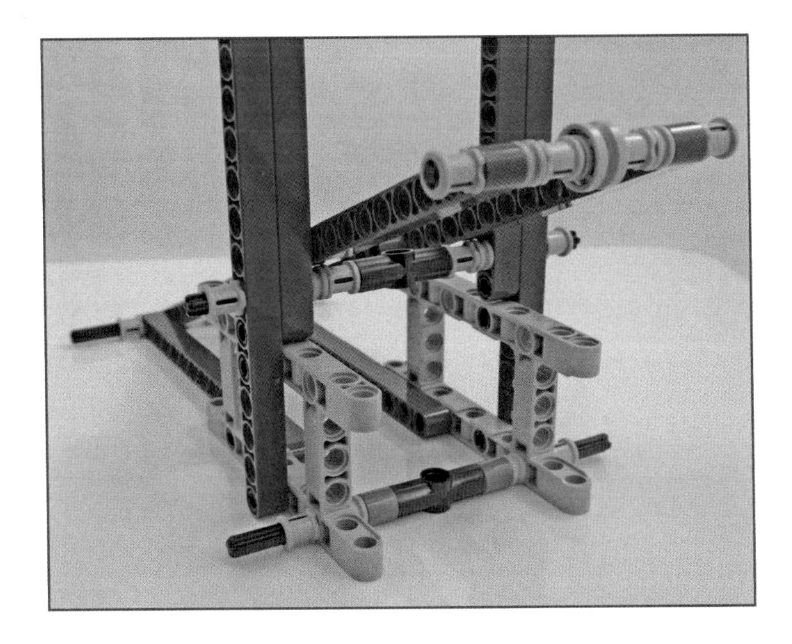

2. Don't bind the parts tightly against the pulley, as it must spin freely.
3. Build the sled and effort force weight and place them on the angle tower, making sure the string runs over the pulley in the proper location.

4. Start with the angle at the lowest angle possible. Note that quite a bit of string hangs off the end, but that's all right. Other experiments will use the same string and will need much more of it. Coil it to one side in such a way that it doesn't interfere with the experiment. Add bricks to the counterweight until the sled begins to move up the incline. Record the number of bricks needed to make this happen.

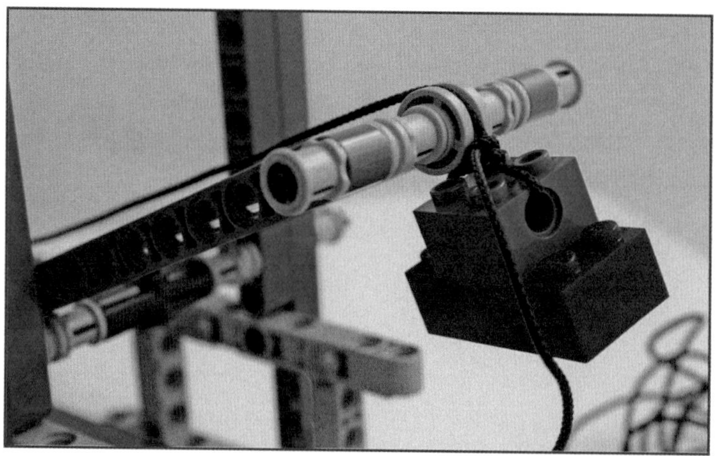

**Angle 2**

5. Increase the incline by moving the stop up 4 holes (3 holes open). Slide the sled back down the incline.
6. Add more weights to the counterweight until the sled begins to move again. Record the number of bricks now needed.

### Angle 3

7. Move the incline to the highest point possible, with the stop down 2 holes.

8. Make sure the sled is at the incline's bottom. Add bricks to the effort force weight until the sled begins to move again. Record the number of bricks needed.

### Inclined Plane Experiments #1: Angles Discussion

You likely found that the sled didn't move with, say four bricks, but slid easily with five. You could test the situation by attaching smaller bricks to fine tune the exact amount of weight required to move the sled. Other than that, this experiment is pretty clear cut: the steeper the angle, the lower the mechanical advantage, which results in the amount of force required to balance and begin to move the sled needing to increase. This would continue all the way until the ramp is vertical, in which case it ceases to be a ramp and you're lifting the object vertically.

Remember, the mechanical advantage of an inclined plane is calculated as follows:

*Mechanical advantage = inclined distance ÷ vertical distance*

Now that you've had a chance to experience this through an experiment, a table can help solidify your understanding:

| Angle (degrees) | Incline Distance (feet) | Vertical Distance (feet) | Mechanical Advantage (incline/vertical) |
|---|---|---|---|
| 10 | 23.0 | 4.0 | 5.76 |
| 20 | 11.7 | 4.0 | 2.92 |
| 45 | 5.7 | 4.0 | 1.41 |
| 60 | 4.6 | 4.0 | 1.15 |
| 80 | 4.1 | 4.0 | 1.02 |
| 90 | 4.0 | 4.0 | 1.00 |

Notice how as the angle increases (90 degrees is vertical), the mechanical advantage decreases. A rating of 1.0 means no help at all.

## Inclined Plane Experiments #2: Parbuckling

Parbuckling, which combines rolling and an inclined plane to move heavy objects, has been around for thousands of years and is still popular today. In fact, you probably have done it yourself and didn't even know it! This isn't really an experiment; it's more an inclined plane application demonstration.

### Parts Needed:

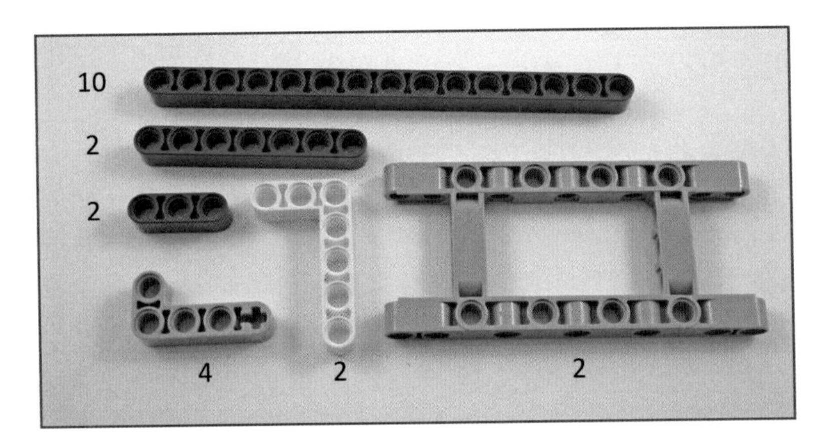


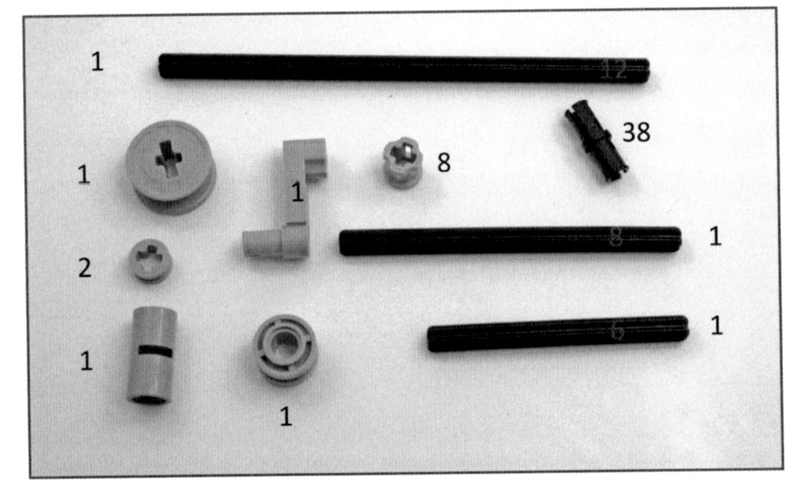


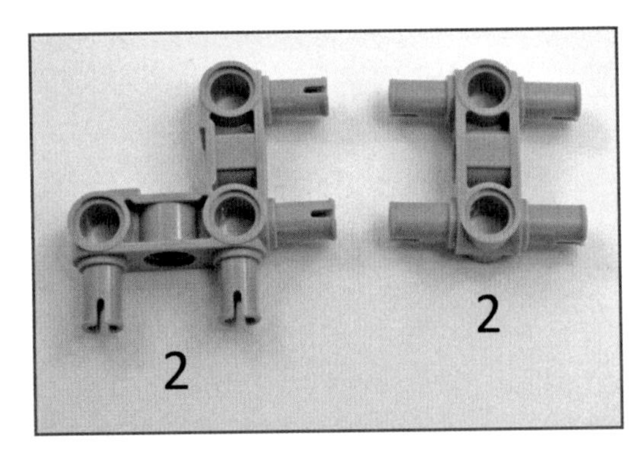

### Procedures:

1. Build the model.

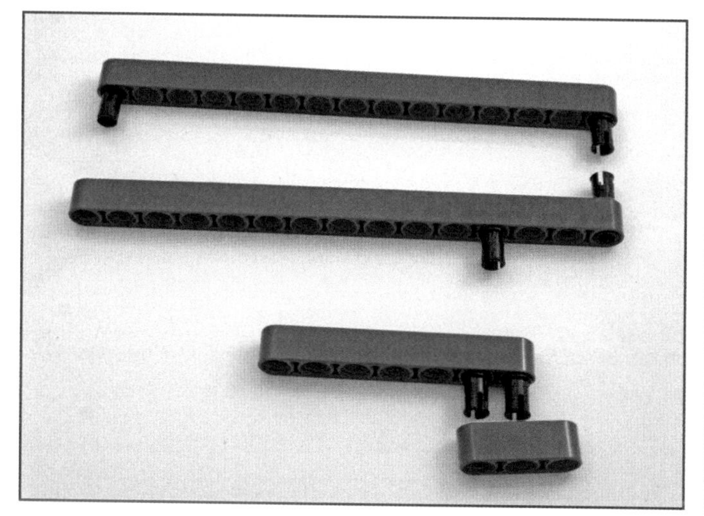

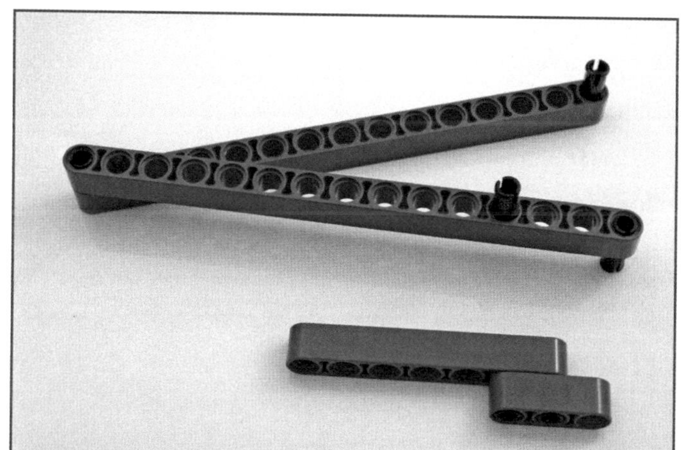

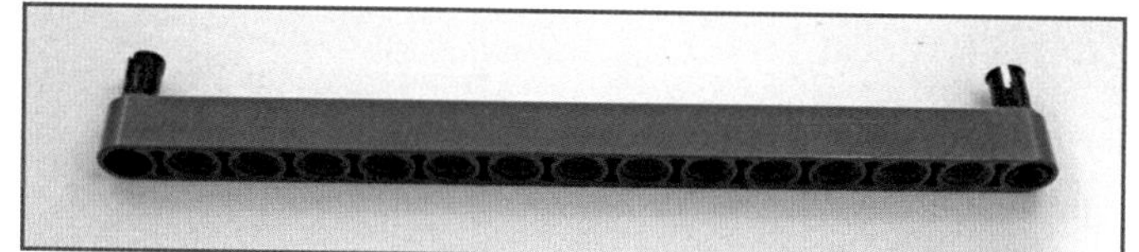

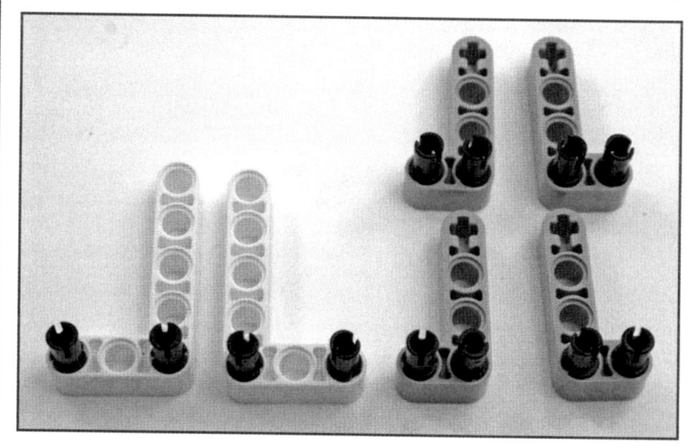

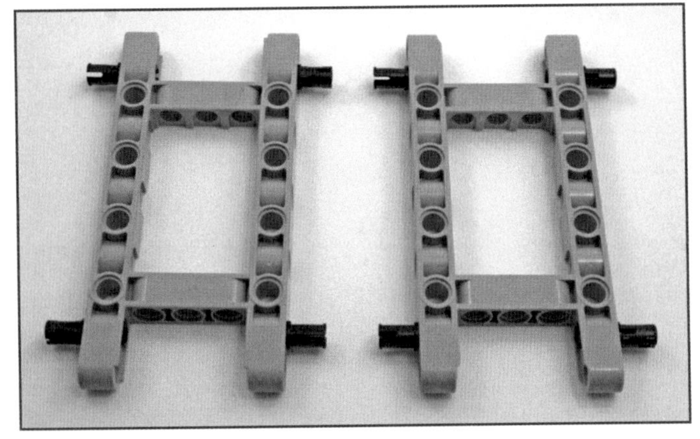

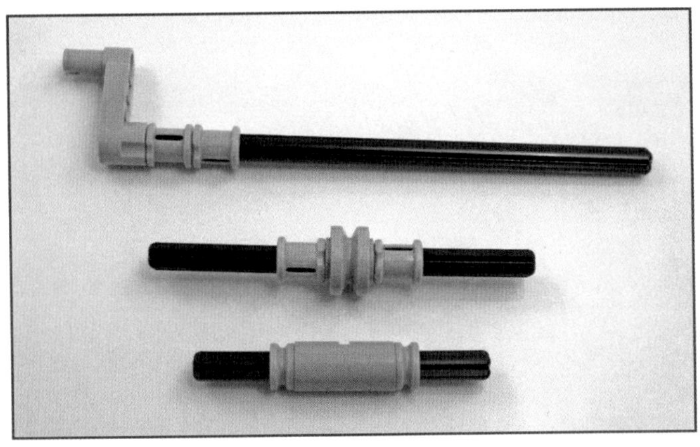

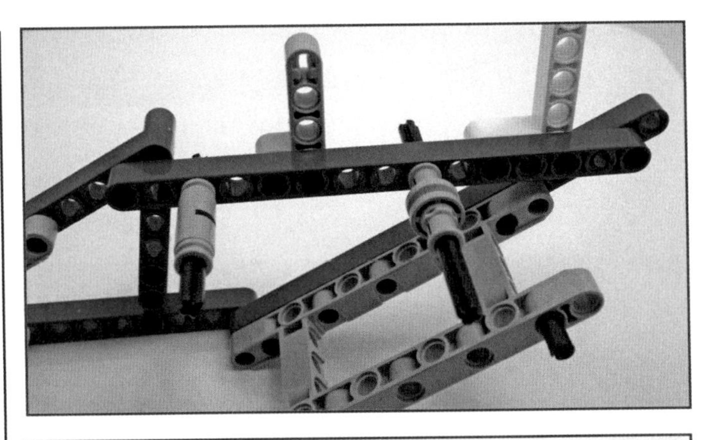

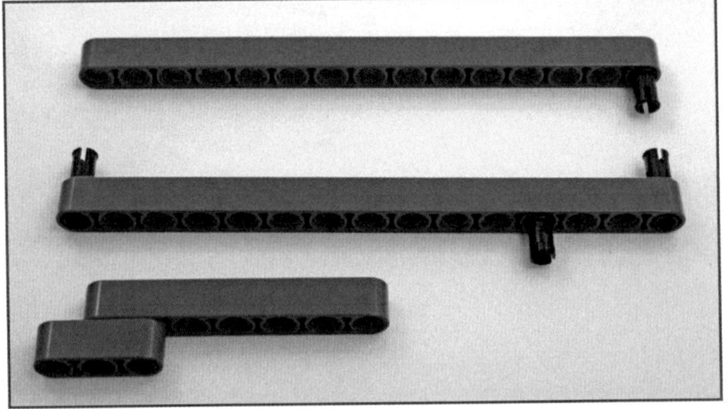

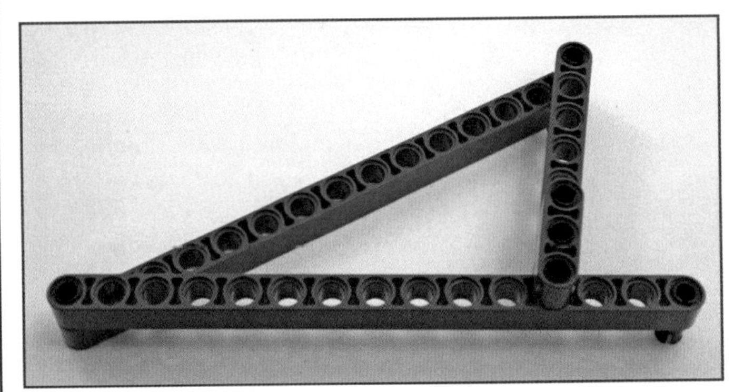

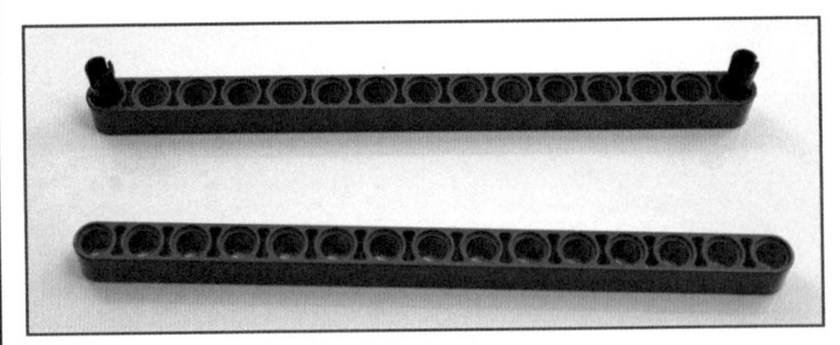

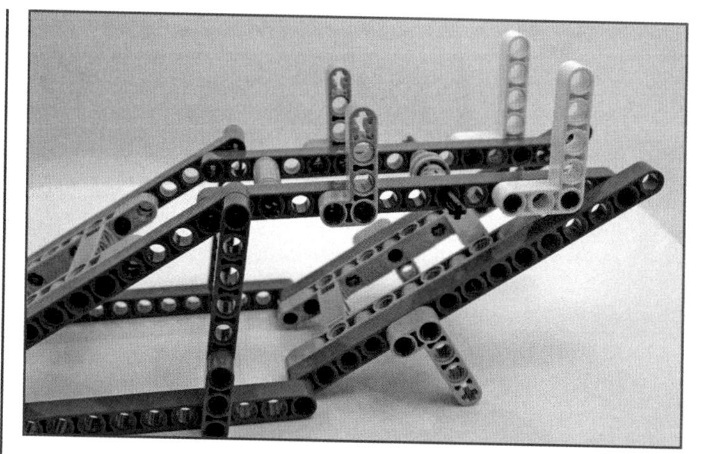

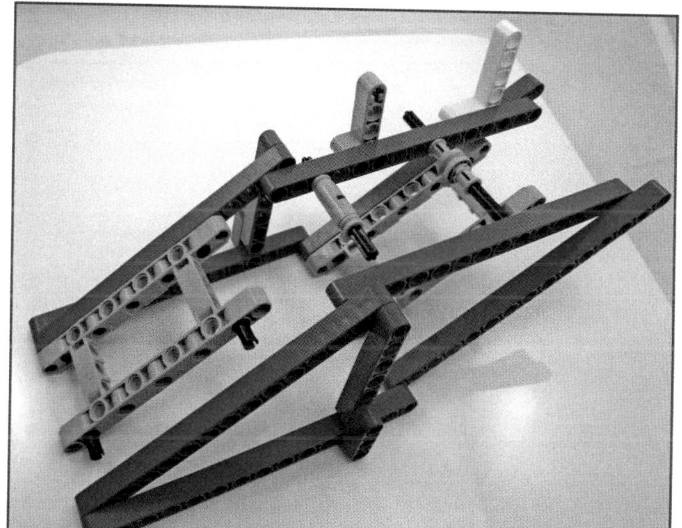

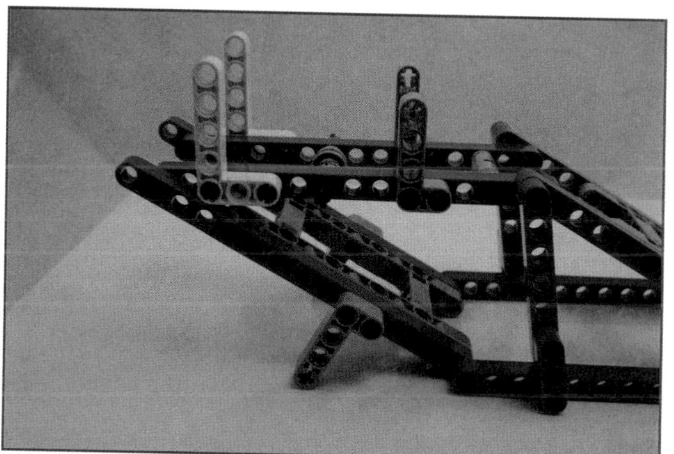

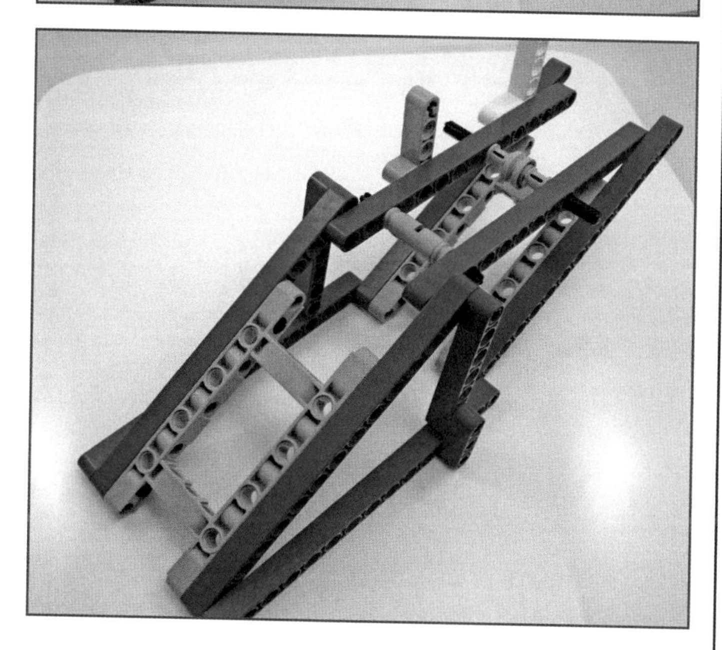

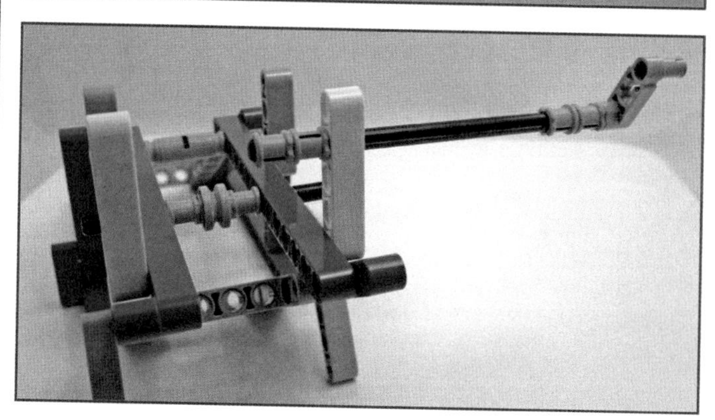

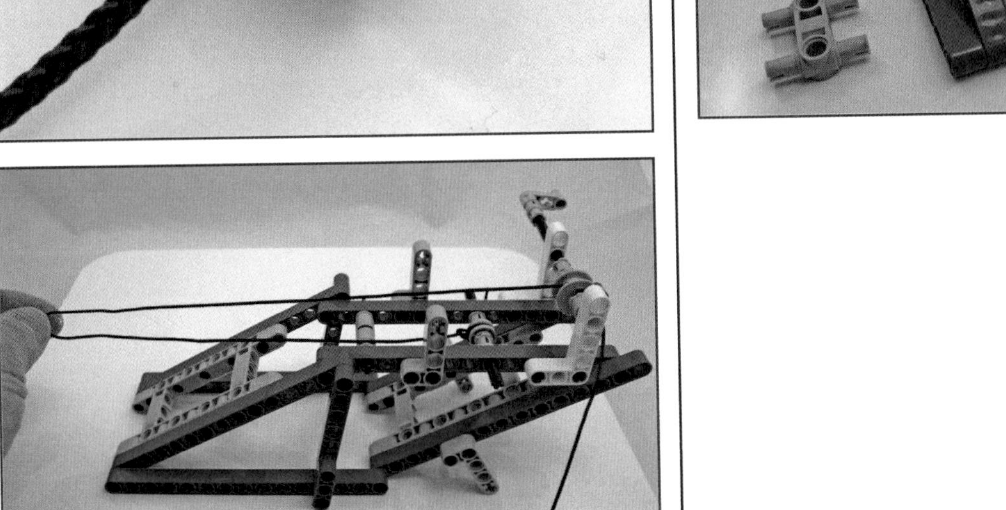

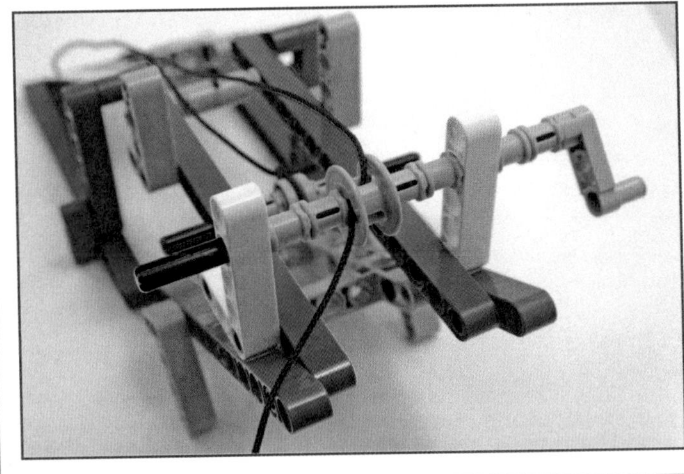

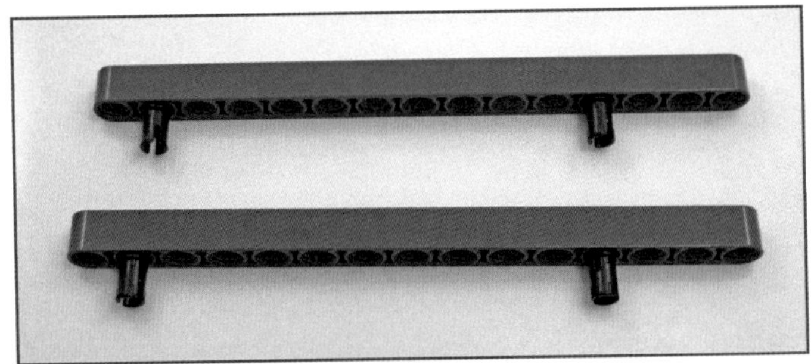

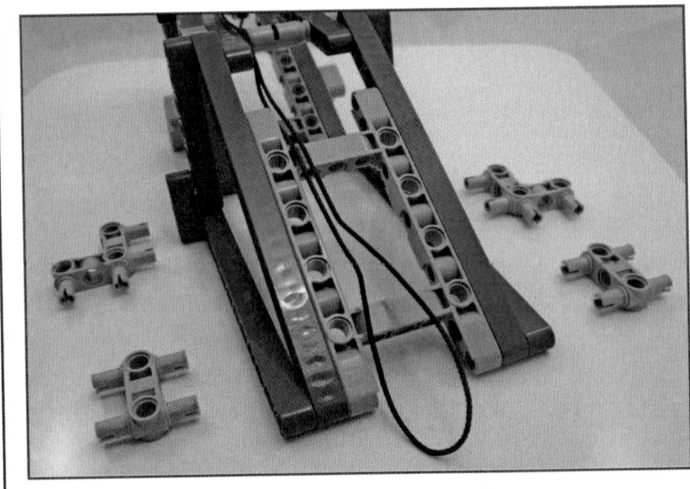

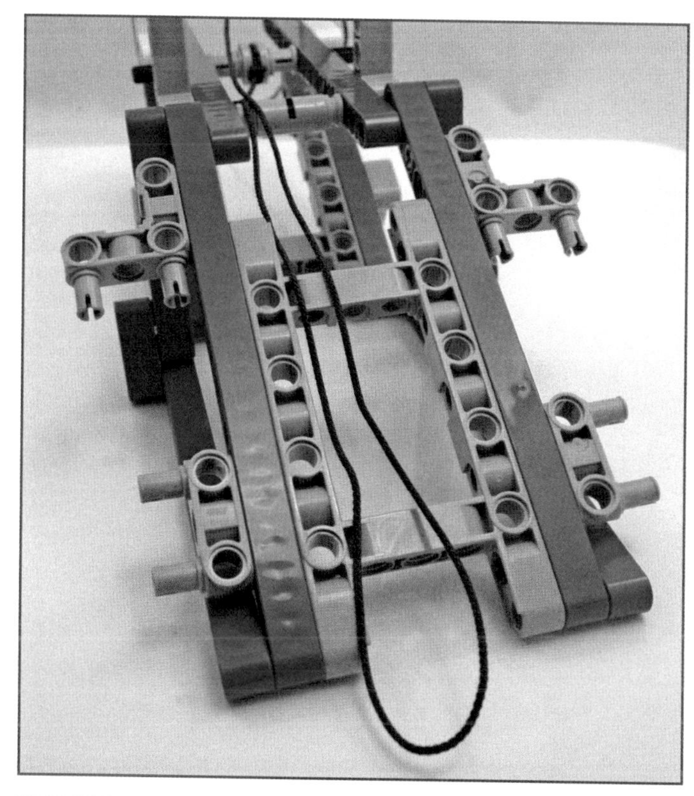

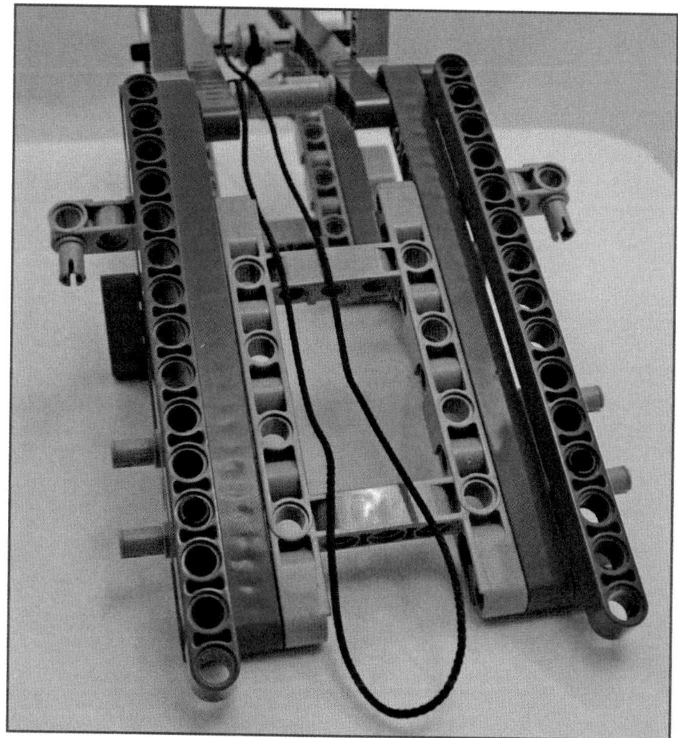

2. Pull the string through the winding spool until the loop just reaches the ramp bottom, then tighten up and position all the pieces.
3. Insert the "log" into the loop, making sure it's between the side rails.

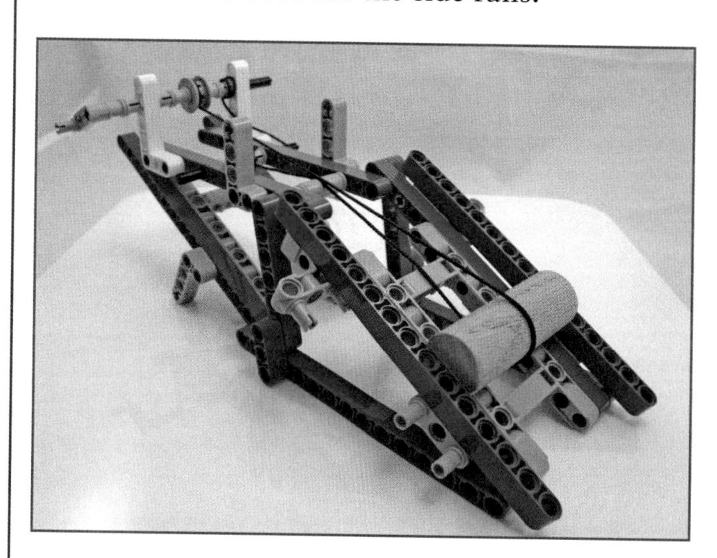

4. Using the winch, roll the log up the inclined plane. Observe how it rolls, and what happens if the string walks off to one side or the other. You will want to adjust the string as the log rolls up, making sure it stays in the log's center. Record your observations:

*Note: the leftover string will wrap itself around the axle, which isn't a problem.*

5. Roll the log all the way to the top. Sometimes it will fall through if it gets turned.

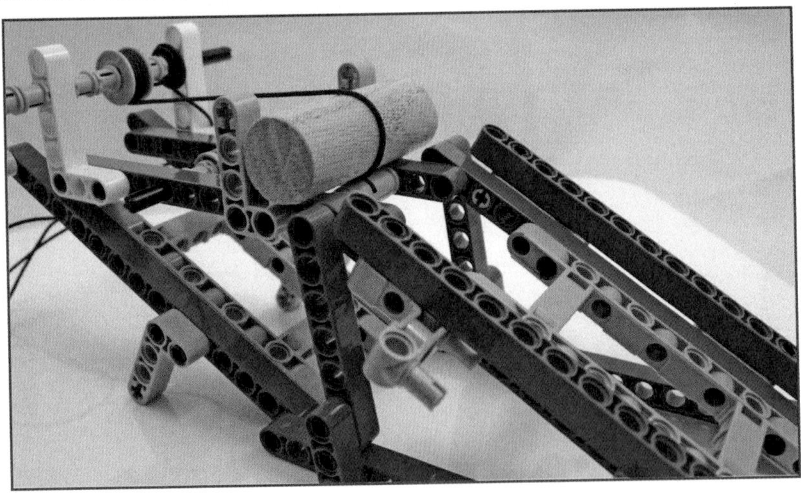

6. Pull the loop back to the ramp bottom with your fingers, unwinding the winch in the process.
7. Using the winch, roll the log about halfway up, then reverse the winch and see if the log rolls back down. Did it work? Why or why not? Record your observations:

8. Continue rolling the log, pulling the loop back down, then rolling it up again. Can you think of ways to improve the design of this parbuckle? Does it make a difference if you wind the winch one way or the other? Record your observations:

The professor who reviewed this workbook, Dr. Lynn Ogden, noted that "when I was a young boy on the farm, we used to roll loose hay off the wagon and up the stack using this [the parbuckle] principle."

### Inclined Plane Experiments #2: Parbuckling Discussion

*Note: If you haven't watched the parbuckling video on page 81, you should prior to reading this discussion. Some of it will not make as much sense without the benefit of having watched the video.*

Due to the scale and complexity of this model, it's difficult to measure differences, but it was included to show a practical application of a ramp and a wheel and axle. Later, the wheel and axle combination is presented in detail and you'll understand a little more of how this machine makes work easier.

The rails on the ramp sides aren't normally part of parbuckling, as you can see in the video. In that example, stabilizing cables end up wrapping around the logs in a V-shape, stabilizing the logs horizontally and preventing them from tipping to one side or the other. I made a model that included these stabilizing "cables" but decided that it was too complex for this workbook. While you were conducting this experiment, you likely noticed the reason for these stabilizing cables: The middle cable sometimes "walks" to one side or the other. Without the rails, the log would become unstable as the center of gravity shifts, and it can fall to one side, slipping through the cable. This would be dangerous in a real-world situation when a heavy log is being moved.

On the other hand, you likely didn't notice a difference winding the winch one way or the other. In a normal parbuckling application, the log being rolled up is heavy, which helps hold the cable taut. Winching up and down the ramp would be easy. In our case, the "log" isn't heavy, and in fact it is insufficiently heavy to pull the string back with it down the ramp. I experimented with other materials, such as a short section of pipe, which more realistically demonstrated the parbuckle. However, cutting these to the right size and removing the sharp edges proved difficult. If you have other materials available to you, both lighter and heavier, try them out. You can even modify your parbuckle to see if you can improve on the design. Email pictures to Beakers & Bricks. We'd love to see what you're doing! We might even share your improvements as suggestions to customers who have purchased this workbook.

Parbuckling is can serve other purposes as well. Some of you may remember the cruise ship *Concordia* that ran aground and partially sank on an Italian coastline, ending up on its side. In order to get it upright again in preparation for floatation, engineers used the same principle as parbuckling logs up a ramp, on a much larger scale. It's pretty ingenious!

**Parbuckling the *Concordia* explained:**
https://www.youtube.com/watch?v=bcNc2CMqNWI
**Watch the actual time-lapse *Concordia* parbuckling event. The engineers righted the ship over several days to avoid inertial forces...the video is therefore a little long!**
https://www.youtube.com/watch?v=RzRgPmRA5PM

**Another example of parbuckling:**
https://www.youtube.com/watch?v=JD1m53UckEk

**An interesting inclined plane elevator:**
https://www.youtube.com/watch?v=-fu03F-lah8&feature=youtu.be

## WHAT DO YOU THINK?

Inclined planes are intuitive. However, the most novel applications of them aren't. For example, it's not common knowledge that a screw and a wedge are both examples of inclined planes. But now you do!

### JOURNALING IDEA

Write as if you were living in a world where the inclined plane hadn't been thought of yet. Describe some challenges you'd face getting around day to day.

### CHAPTER REVIEW

1. Take a drive through town and notice any inclined planes that you see. Make a list of at least five.
2. Can you think of ways to reduce friction when moving a heavy object across a surface?
3. How do you think people invented tools that existed prior to electric power and motors? Why did they invent the tools?
4. Are stairs an example of an inclined plane? Explain.
5. Look at the different knives you have in your kitchen. Disregarding length, how are they different from one another? Why do you think the differences exist?

**Another boating example of parbuckling:**
https://www.youtube.com/watch?v=ov0jXYoYM8s

# CHAPTER 4

# SIMPLE MACHINES: THE WHEEL AND AXLE

The wheel and axle is another simple machine invented long ago that improves our lives in countless ways. The wheel and axle doesn't have to be exactly that, either. The same principle is applicable to a rolling cylinder.

The wheel and axle has two basic configurations: where the speed is multiplied and where the force is multiplied. Both measurements depend on where the effort force is applied.

## MULTIPLYING SPEED

As shown to the right, the speed is multiplied by an increase in effort force to the axle. A large rotary force applied at the axle causes the larger circumference wheel to turn, with the speed at its edge greatly increased relative to the rotational speed of the axle. A wheel and axle is also an example of a first-class lever, with the fulcrum between the effort and load forces.

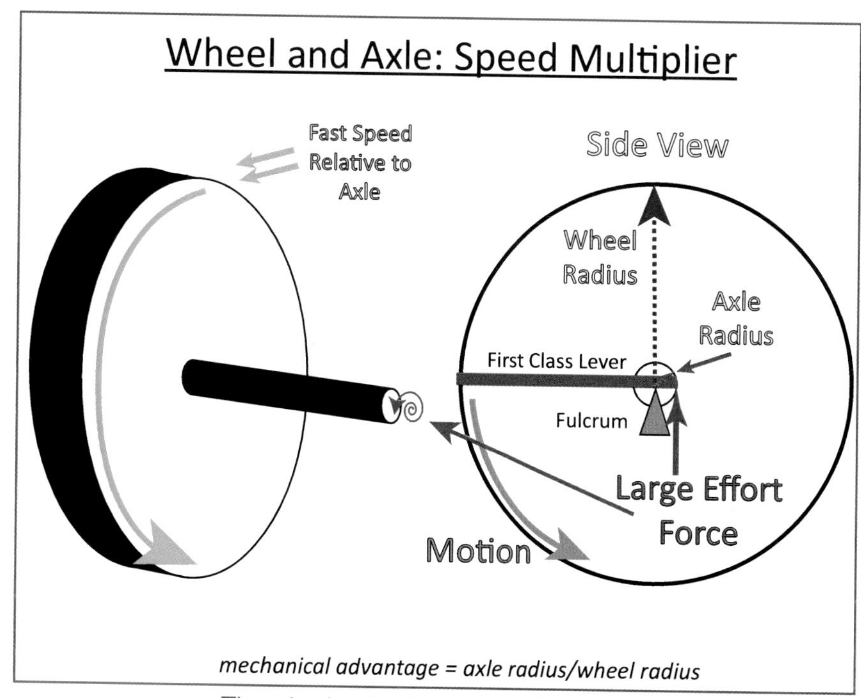

The wheel and axle as a speed multiplier

The mechanical advantage can be calculated as:

*Mechanical advantage = input ÷ output = axle radius ÷ wheel radius*

Let's plug in some numbers and see how this works. We'll assign a radius of 3 inches to the axle and 24 inches to the wheel:

*Mechanical advantage = 3 ÷ 24 = 0.125*

You can see that a larger force is required at the axle to get the wheel to spin. However, the rotational velocity (also called "angular velocity") at the wheel's outside diameter is much greater than the axle's rotational velocity. Think again of the formula *Work = force x distance*. In this case, turning the axle is moving a small distance, and therefore the force must be increased to accomplish the same amount of work.

Examples of this type of arrangement are axles and wheels on vehicles (of course!), and gears. While the special application of the wheel and axle to gears will be covered in the last chapter, let's look in detail about how the wheel and axle work.

## MULTIPLYING FORCE

When the opposite side of the first-class lever in the wheel is used, applying force to the wheel's outside that is transferred to the axle, force is multiplied.

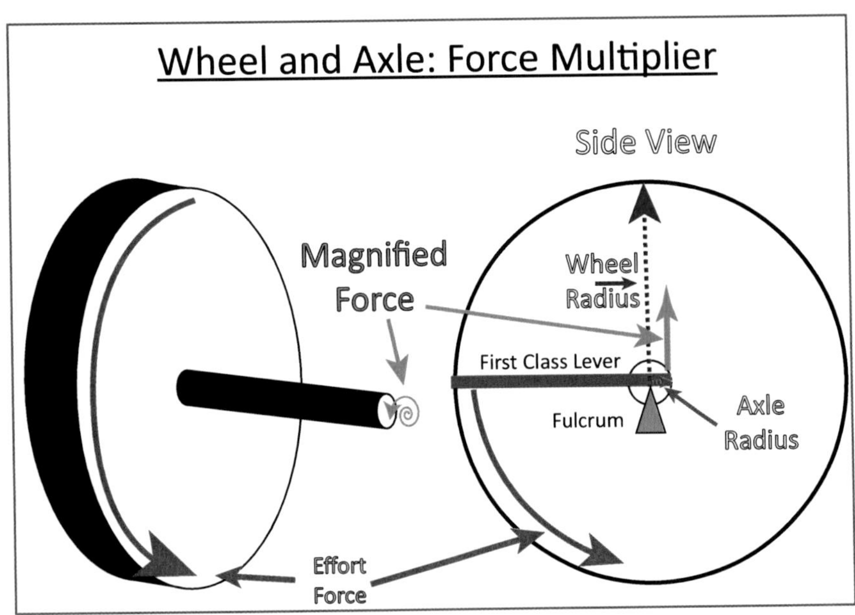


The wheel and axle as a force multiplier

The same simple machine principle applies: effort force is decreased by increasing the distance traveled by that effort force. Again, looking at *Work = force x distance*, the wheel's outside moves much farther than the axle. Therefore, the same work can be performed by much less effort.

Conversely, the same effort can produce much more work. We can calculate the mechanical advantage:

*Mechanical advantage = input ÷ output = wheel radius ÷ axle radius*

We'll use the same radii as our previous example: 3 inches for the axle and 24 inches for the wheel.

*Mechanical advantage = 24 inches ÷ 3 inches = 8*

This means that the same force is multiplied 8 times!

As an example, consider a screwdriver. With its tip in a screw head, you turn the handle. The larger diameter handle turns a greater distance, exerting leverage on the smaller diameter screw.

In addition to the screwdriver, other not-so-obvious examples of the same wheel and axle force multiplication principles are doorknobs, winches, gears, and pulleys. Let's investigate how pulleys work.

## PULLEYS

Pulleys are a special wheel and axle where a groove around the wheel holds a rope or cable to transfer force. Pulleys can be fixed or can move depending on their configuration, and there can be single or multiple pulleys in the same tool. When more than one pulley is combined, they're usually called a "block" of pulleys, and the rope or cable running through them is referred to as "tackle." The combined tool is commonly referred to as "block and tackle."

A pulley

### Fixed Pulleys

A fixed pulley is the simplest of all pulleys, primarily functioning to change the effort force's direction. While no mechanical advantage is associated with a fixed single pulley, instead of having to haul the cable or rope up, you can pull it down toward the ground and the load moves up.

Contrary to what you may think, changing the direction of needed force toward the ground via a single fixed pulley doesn't necessarily allow gravity to help, unless a weight is the effort force. For example, a weight can be hung on the effort force side. If the weight is heavy enough, it will pull the load up, with the amount of force needed no different than if you were pulling the load straight up. Even so, the change in direction allows flexibility in where force is applied.

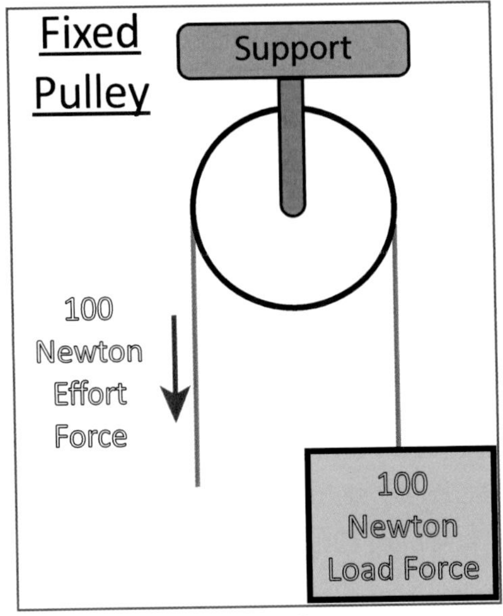

A fixed pulley

### Movable Pulleys

A single movable pulley changes the effort force's direction, but also has a mechanical advantage, halving the amount of force required to lift the weight. In this case, the 100 newton weight requires only 50 newtons effort force to be vertically lifted.

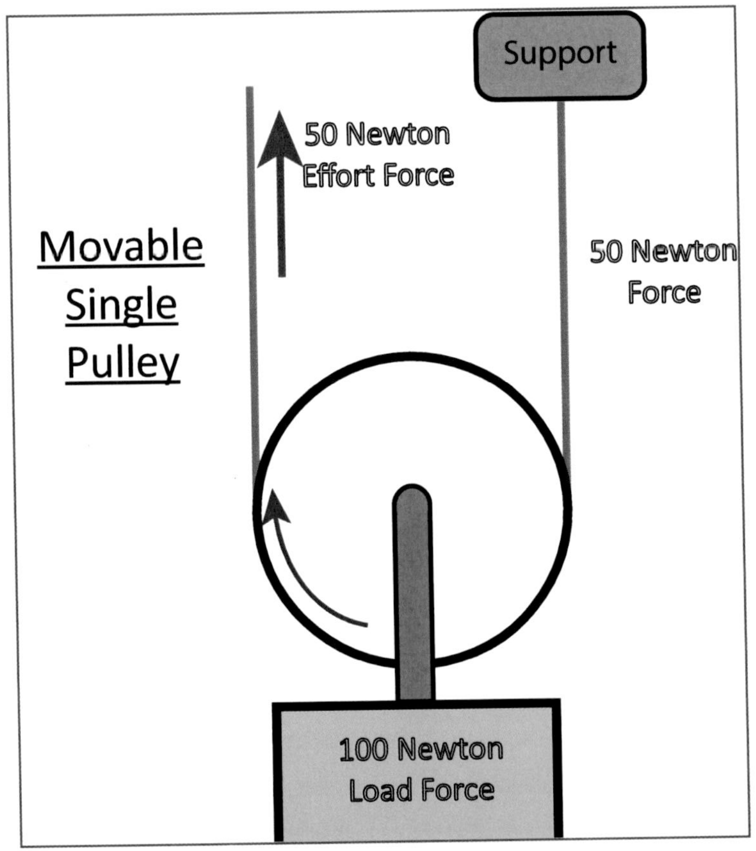

Movable single pulleys

A compound pulley can have a fixed and a movable pulley as well, as in this configuration:

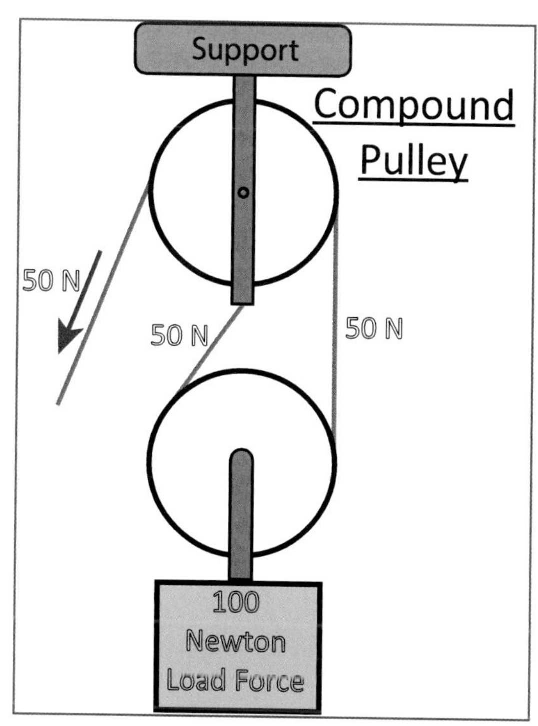

Compound pulleys

The effort force required for this compound pulley is no different than the single movable pulley that only changes the force's direction, requiring 50 newtons to lift the 100 newton load force.

> ***Pulley rule of thumb:*** A good rule that usually holds true is the effort force needed to hold a load force in a pulley system is equal to the load force divided by the number of ropes between the pulleys.

### Block and Tackle

Let's look at one other configuration, and this one is quite common: the block and tackle. As mentioned earlier, a block combines two or more pulleys into one block of pulleys, and the tackle is the rope or cable running through the blocks. In the illustrated case, the effort force needed is the load force divided by 4.

One block & tackle example

The mechanical advantage can be expressed this way:

*Pulley mechanical advantage = distance the effort rope travels ÷ distance the object is lifted*

You'll see this in an experiment later.

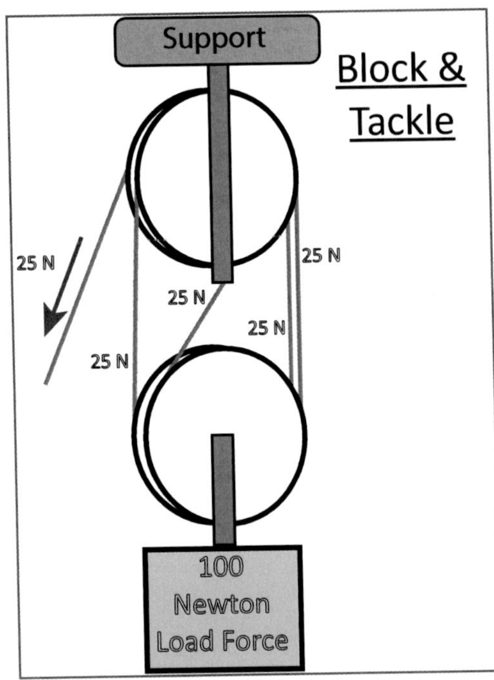

The block & tackle

## Other Pulley Considerations

You should note that all the illustrations just discussed are assuming the system is at rest. In other words, nothing is moving—everything is *static*. We know from Newton's first law that inertia is an important consideration. Using the last block and tackle example, with the system at rest, it takes more than 25 newtons to get the 100 newton mass moving. How quickly that effort force is applied—or in other words, the rate of acceleration—has a great effect on the tension or strain put on the equipment. It's even worse if you try to reverse the direction while the mass is moving, for the same reasoning within the law of inertia. That's why cranes lifting heavy objects move slowly: to prevent any unexpected momentary acceleration-related strains or stresses that might take their equipment past its design specifications and result in a failure.

**Here's another video that shows the trade-off between force and distance in pulley systems:**
https://www.youtube.com/watch?v=73vnrGYmS5U

***Static:*** In this situation, a system that's stable and not moving; in equilibrium.

Pulleys are another great example of trading force for distance. Since *Work = force x distance,* we know that to reduce the force, we have to exert that reduced force over a longer distance. For pulley systems, this phenomenon is evident through sometimes running a LOT of rope or cable through cable blocks to move a weight a relatively small distance. A later experiment shows this firsthand.

## EXPERIMENTS: LET'S BUILD SOMETHING!

In these series of experiments, single, multiple, fixed, and movable pulleys and pulley blocks are built and tested. The tower built in Experiment #1 is needed in all three.

### Wheel and Axle Experiment #1: Single Pulley, Attached Directly to Load

### Parts List:

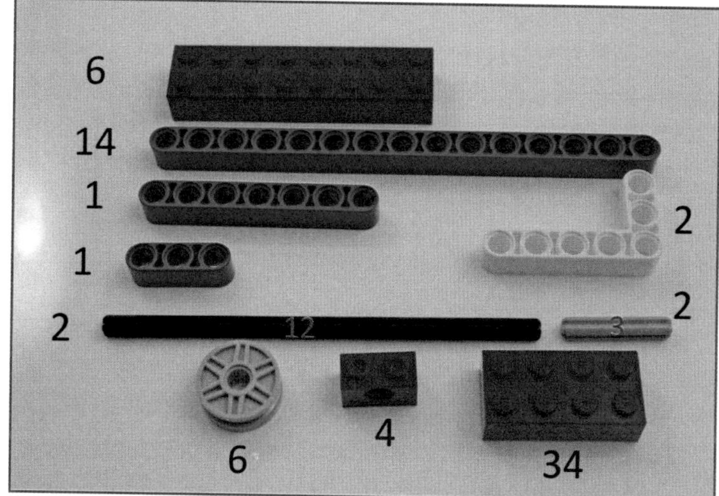

**Procedures:**

1. Build the tower.

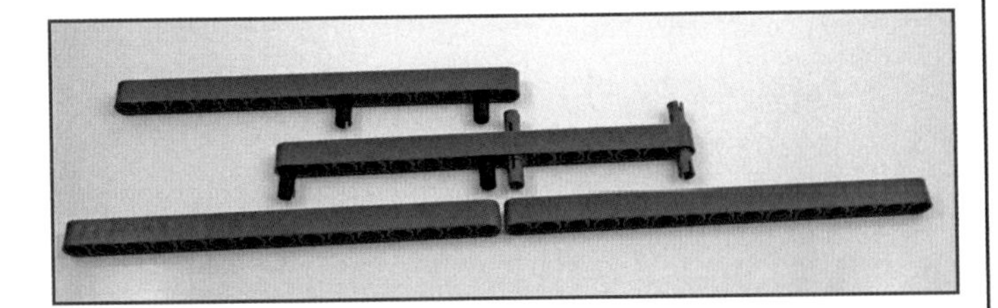

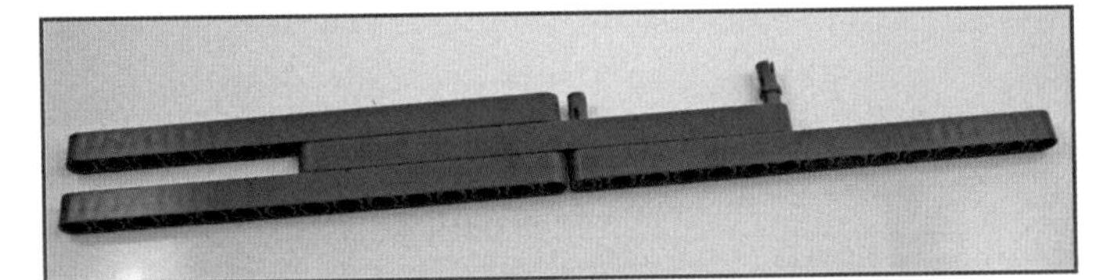

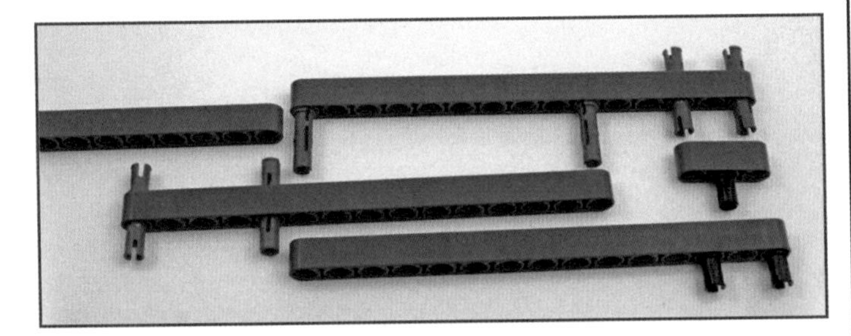

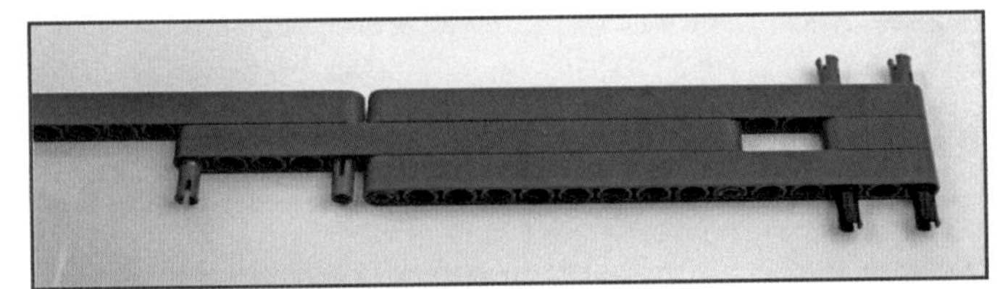

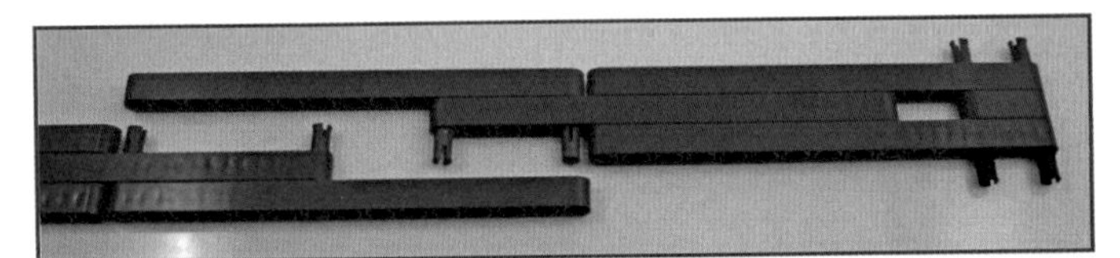

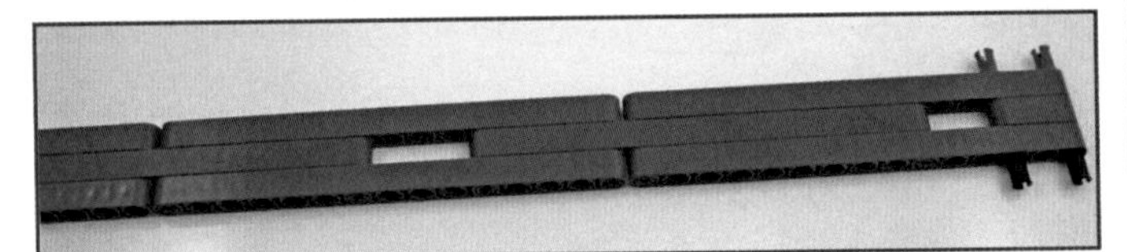

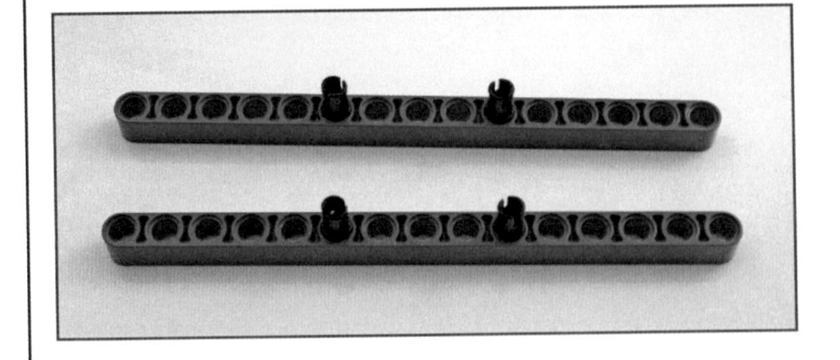

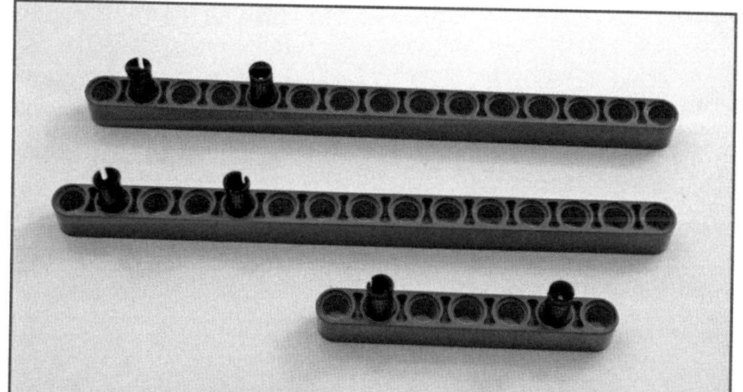

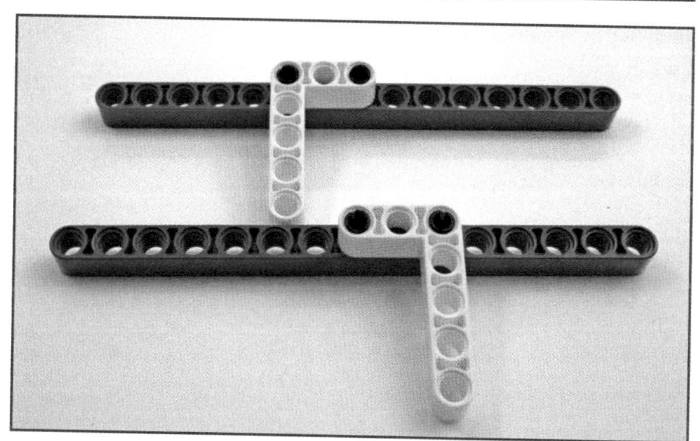

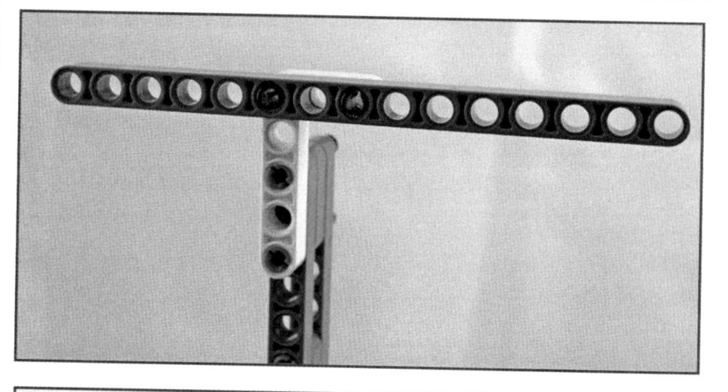

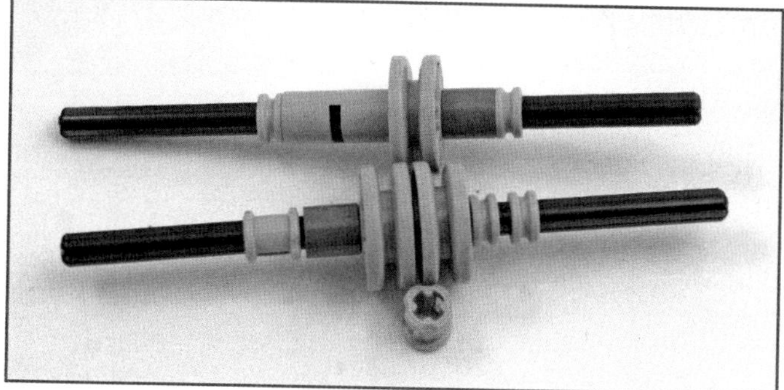

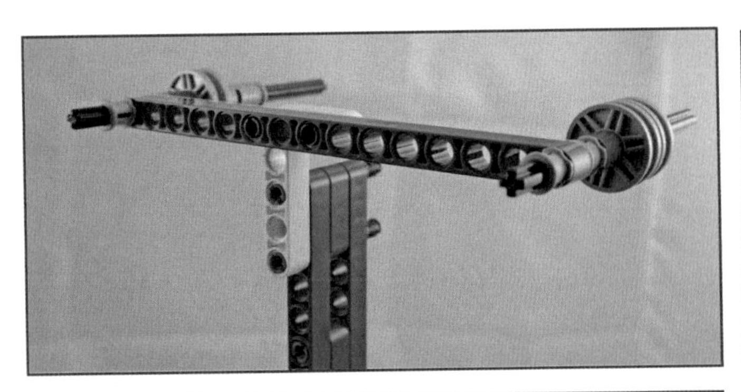

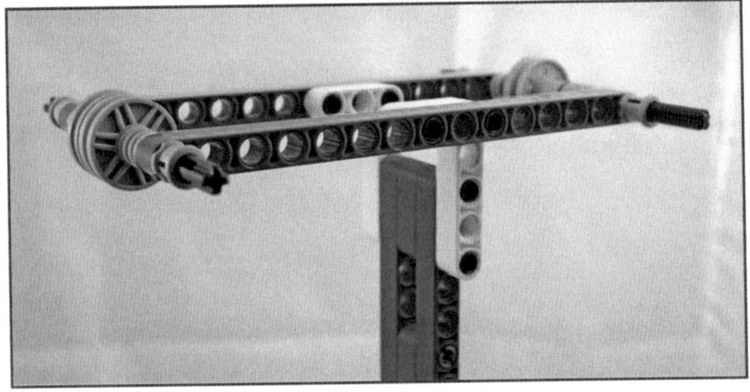

2. Build the load weight (load force).

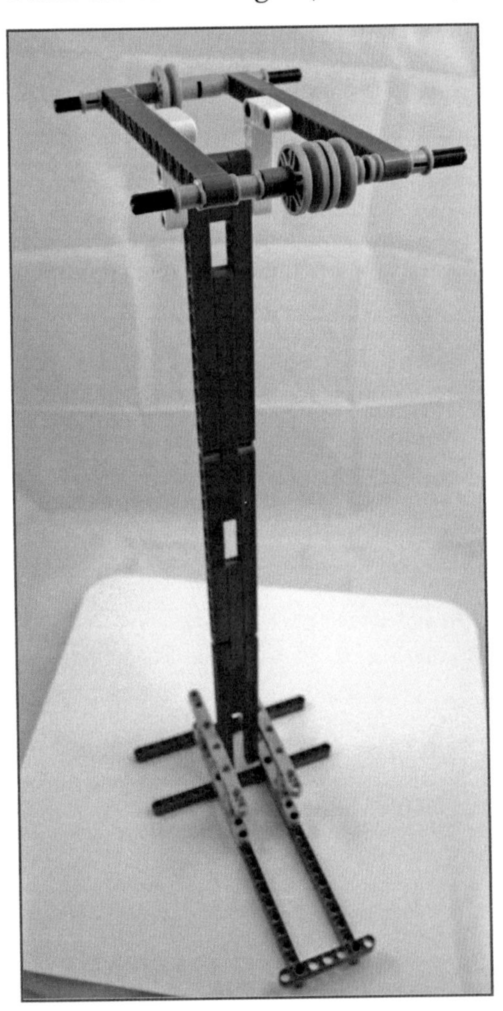

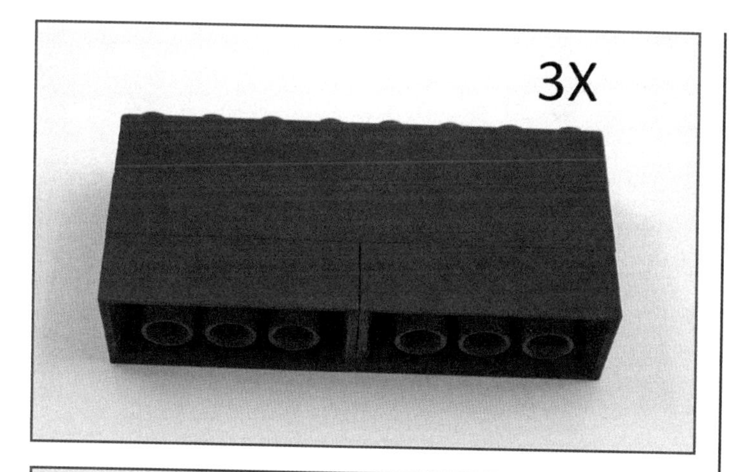

3. Attach the string by tying it around the load pulley.

4. Build the counterweight (effort weight or effort force).

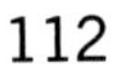

5. Make sure all the pulleys spin freely and aren't bound. If needed, adjust the other parts away from the pulleys slightly to allow for free movement.

6. We're ready to begin the first exercise (finally)!
7. Attach the string to the counterweight by running it up and over the pulleys, tying it off with the counterweight very close to the tower pulley.

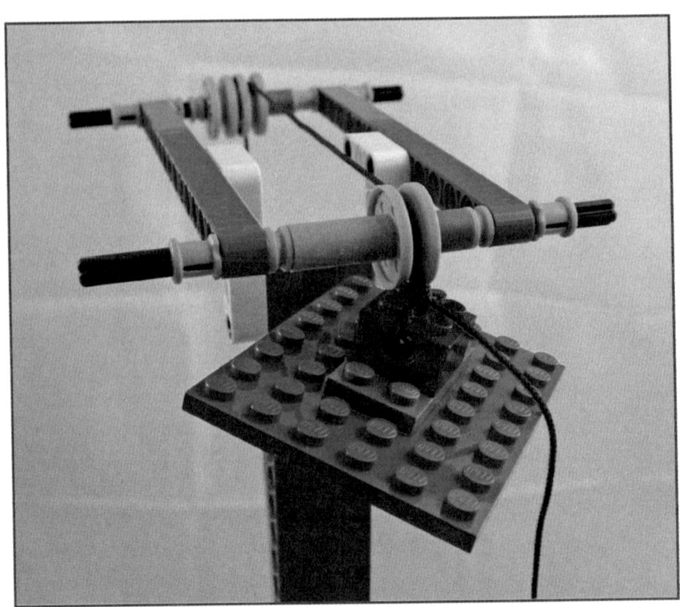

8. Make sure that the string is on the pulley and not in between pulleys or neighboring parts. Any added friction in the system due to this or other reasons will affect your results.

9. Attach the red 2x4 bricks to the counterweight until the load weight begins to lift. Lift the weight platform, remove one brick, and try it again, making sure the

string is in the right tracks.

10. Count the number of bricks and record the data, along with your observations. Pay particular attention to how far the string moves on the counterweight side relative to the load. You can use a ruler to measure the distance the counterweight moves, and the same for the load.

11. Remove the bricks from the counterweight.

### Wheel and Axle Experiment #1: Single Pulley, Attached Directly to Load Discussion

You should have noticed the counterweight needing about the same weight that exists on the load weight. The bricks aren't exactly the same here, as the load weight has some 2x8 bricks that weigh slightly less than two 2x4 bricks. The load side also has more rigging, with the pulley and associated pieces.

The principle of this configuration is that if there were no frictional differences between sides and no rigging differences, an equal load on both sides would result in a balanced system, not moving either way. The weights won't be exactly the same, but they're close. This type of configuration changes the effort force's direction even though there's no mechanical advantage.

### Wheel and Axle Experiment #2: Compound Pulley

1. Remove the string from the counterweight and the load. Tie the string to the tower, loop through the counterweight pulley, up and over the tower pulleys. Tie the other string end to the counterweight, again close to the pulley on the tower. (Note: in the picture, the counterweight has bricks attached, whereas as per the instructions, at this point yours shouldn't have any.)

2. Add 2x4 bricks to the counterweight again until the load begins to rise. Remove one brick from the counterweight and repeat the exercise. Record the number of bricks and your observations. As before, measure the distance the counterweight and load travel.

### Wheel and Axle Experiment #2: Compound Pulley Discussion

This was quite different than Experiment #1. The load moved about half the distance as the counterweight, and the amount of bricks needed was a lot less. The mechanical advantage here was 2, which means that the effort force needed is about half of a direct lift. The extra "distance traveled" by the rigging needs to be accounted for. The spool would have to be big enough to hold the cable and move the load to the desired location.

### Wheel and Axle Experiment #3: Block and Tackle

1. Remove the bricks from the counterweight again, and rebuild load force weight as pictured:

2. Route the string through the pulleys as shown:

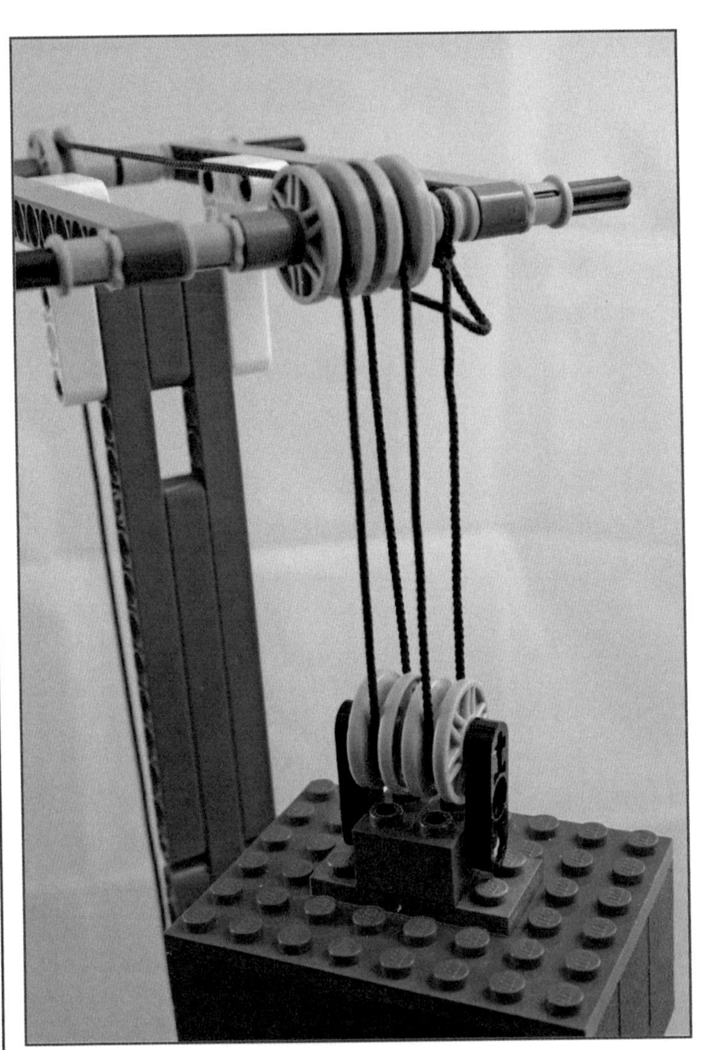

3. As before, add 2x4 bricks to the counterweight until the load starts to lift. Remove a brick and repeat the exercise, making sure the string runs through the correct tracks. Measure the distance the counterweight travels and the distance the load travels. Record your observations, the number of bricks needed to move the load, and the distances traveled by the counterweight and the load.

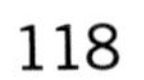

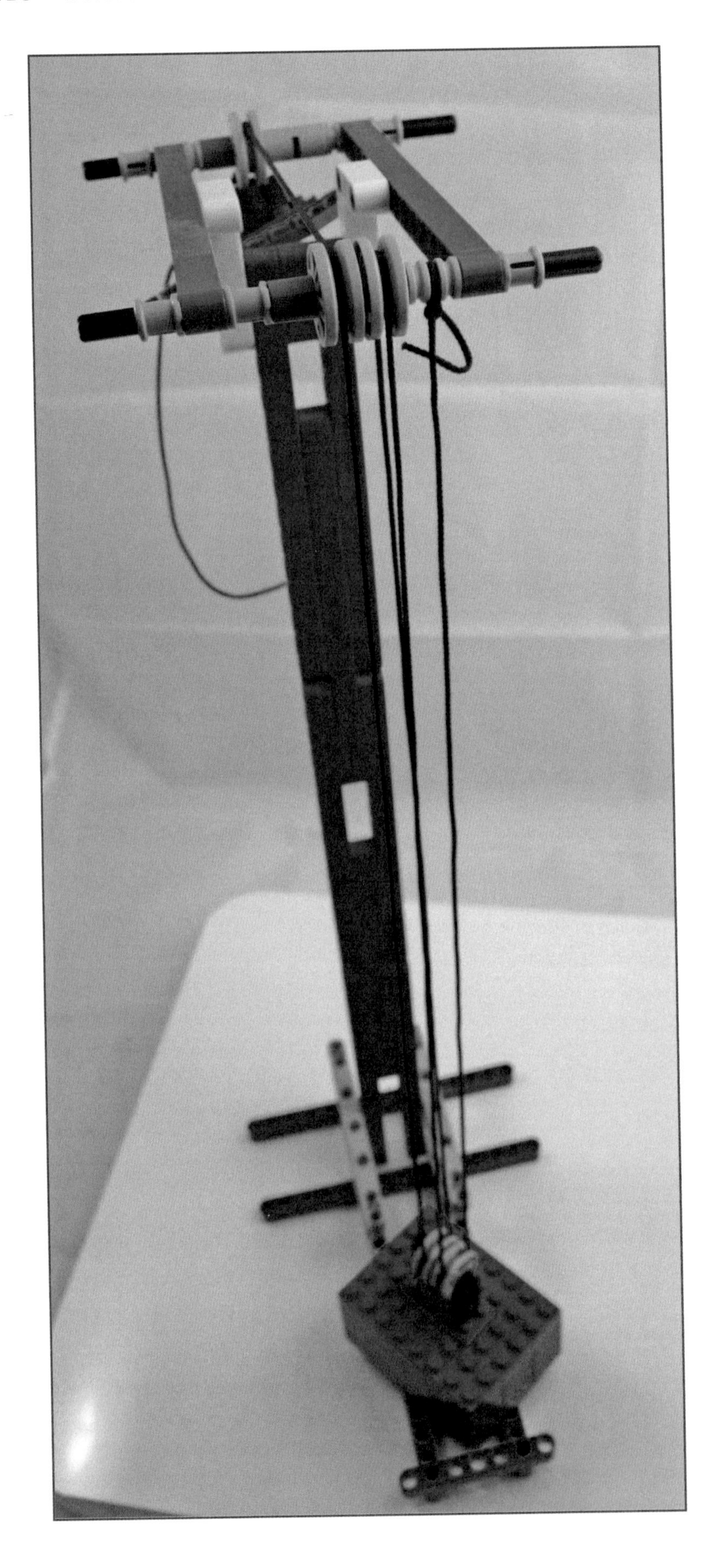

### Wheel and Axle Experiment #3: Block and Tackle Discussion

A block and tackle is how small motors can move heavy weights. Cranes, for example, use blocks that have lots of pulleys, resulting in a very large mechanical advantage. The trade-off, as you know by now, is distance. The weight hardly moves at all with a corresponding large movement on the counterweight side. In the case of this experiment, the mechanical advantage was 4, which means only 1/4 of the normally needed force was needed.

See if you can modify the model. For example, you could add a winch that allows you to move the load all the way to the tower top!

## WHAT DO YOU THINK?

The wheel and axle and the pulley are sometimes considered separate simple machines, and sometimes not. The wheel and axle principle is the same. Gears are closely related to the wheel and axle and are discussed in the next chapter. You might write another introductory physics book someday and think of a different way to present the subject that works better!

## JOURNALING IDEA

Pretend you live in a world without wheels and axles. Review your activities for one day, identifying everything you use that involves that simple machine. Describe how your day would be different without them, including how you might accomplish the same tasks.

## CHAPTER REVIEW

1. Think of a screwdriver. Draw a cross section showing the lever and where the force is applied. Is it the same for a doorknob?
2. List at least three other axle and wheel examples.
3. Go back to the parbuckle experiment. What kind and where are the levers in that complex machine?
4. Explain how a crank handle uses the axle and wheel mechanical advantage to accomplish work.

# CHAPTER 5
# TRANSFER OF ENERGY

**As we've seen, machines are designed** to move energy from a point of generation to a point where it is needed, and most often to also magnify the energy input through mechanical leverage.

Potential energy can be transformed in all kinds of ways, including directly from falling water through a water wheel; through combustion of materials that convert water to steam, which turns turbines to generate electricity; or even with gas-powered engines that turn an axle with attached wheels.

Figuring out and describing how energy moves through a system to the object that accomplishes a useful task is the work of engineers. Simplistically, all machines involve energy transfer.

Examples include gears, universal joints, axles and wheels, and hydraulics. We'll briefly look at each (excluding wheels and axles, which we've al-

A water wheel[26]

ready talked about), and a couple of them in some depth.

## UNIVERSAL JOINTS

Whether you know it or not, you've seen universal joints. When you're at a stoplight next to a truck that's higher off the ground, they're readily visible.

Universal joint on a truck

This machine allows for the continuous transfer of energy with a limited change in longitudinal direction. It permits movement at one end or the other, and that's why it's common in situations such as the one pictured. In this case, the axle and truck wheel move up and down as the truck travels and encounters uneven pavement, potholes, etc. If the shaft was connected directly to the axle, the system would be destroyed in short order. You'll get to try universal joints in the experiments section.

## HYDRAULICS

Another way to transfer energy is through hydraulics. Hydraulic power is how much of the earthmoving and lifting tasks in the world today are accomplished. Hydraulics function by transferring energy via fluids through flexible hoses, and the movement being accomplished through hydraulic cylinders.

A pump pressurizes the hydraulic fluid, usually a type of oil, which moves the cylinders in and out.

Fluids compress very little. Similar equipment to hydraulics is used with pressurized air, with advantages and disadvantages existing for both. Air has to be highly compressed to function similar to hydraulics.

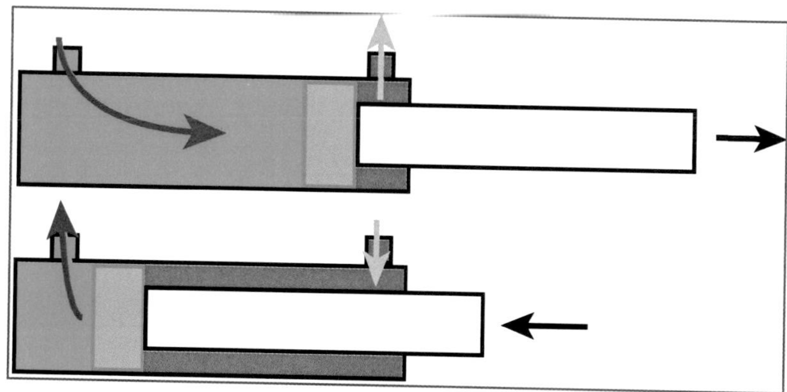

Hydraulic cylinder illustration

The cylinder is composed of a shaft attached to a piston, with the piston enclosed in a cylinder. Seals associated with the piston, and where the shaft moves in and out of the cylinder, minimize hydraulic fluid leakage. Stated simply, a hydraulic pump pressurizes the fluid, and valves control the flow to the piston's faces (down or upstroke). Whichever side receives the flow pressurizes, moving the cylinder, and hydraulic fluid exits from the piston's other side.

In the illustration, the cylinder is green. The fluid on either side is depicted as colored to emphasize which side is receiving the flow, when in reality, it's the same fluid being pulled from the same reservoir.

**While this is an old video, hydraulic concepts are described well, and some examples are shown:** https://www.youtube.com/watch?v=rkiBikJuWyE

Pictured is what's called a "4-in-1 bucket." It has the ability to scoop and dig like a bucket, but also clamp and bulldoze. In this picture, a cylinder is indicated by the yellow arrow. The hydraulic fluid is supplied to this cylinder through the hydraulic lines indicated by the red arrow.

A hydraulic 4-in-1 bucket

A good example is a compact loader.

Dale's compact loader

Compact loaders are essentially a large motor on wheels or tracks that powers hydraulic pumps. Tens, if not hundreds, of attachments are made for the compact loader. They're kind of like the construction industry's Swiss Army knife!

**A video of me demonstrating my compact track loader and some of the equipment I use on it, and examples of how they are used!**
https://www.youtube.com/watch?v=iVYX6Dg6MrA

**A 4-in-1 bucket description and demonstration on a compact loader:**
https://www.youtube.com/watch?v=FLAIgzCKfe8&t=90s

## GEARS

Gears are a special wheel and axle application, with a lot of possible variety. We've already talked about how in a wheel and axle, depending on where the effort force is applied, the result can be either a force multiplier or speed multiplier. The same principle applies for gears: The energy transfer happens at gears' circumferences, which can be freely spinning on a fixed axle or attached for further energy transfer. Some examples are pictured.

Gears[27]

An automobile transmission[28]

Gears can be simple or complex, from a can opener to an automobile transmission. They all work in different fashions to transfer energy from the source to where it's needed.

Different from pulleys, an important consideration is that with each successive gear in a configuration, the direction of rotation changes. In this sense, gears are a tool for changing the direction of an effort force. You will get to experience several different configurations in the experiment section.

***Driver gear:*** The gear providing the effort force.
***Follower gear:*** The gear receiving the effort force.

## Number of Teeth

Since gears have teeth, it's possible to make action predictions. For example, one gear has 24 teeth and the other 8 teeth:

- If the 24-tooth gear is the driver gear and the 8-tooth gear the follower, the 8-tooth gear has to spin much faster to "keep up" with the 24-tooth driver gear.
- If the 8-tooth gear is the driver and the 24-tooth the follower, the reverse happens. The 24-tooth gear will spin much more slowly than the 8-tooth driver gear.

It's also possible to determine the mechanical advantage by counting the number of teeth on intermeshing gears. A common term is "gear ratio," which refers to the ratio of the follower gear to the driven gear. In our example, assuming the follower is the 24-tooth, it's a 24/8 ratio or, getting to the least common denominator, a 3/1 gear ratio, more commonly written as a 3:1 gear ratio.

With the reverse—the 8-tooth gear as the follower—it would be an 8/24, or 1:3 gear ratio.

*Gear ratio = follower gear ÷ driver gear*

Or:

*Gear ratio = number of follower gear teeth ÷ number of driver gear teeth*

> ***Gear trains:*** When more than two gears are connected in a path together, it's called a gear train.
> ***Drive train:*** In automobiles, the whole process of producing and transferring power to the axle is called the drive train. It includes the engine, transmission, differential gears, and axles, among other things.

Remember (again!), *Work = force x distance.* In the case of a high gear ratio (the follower gear has more teeth), the driver gear has to turn more (more distance at the circumference) to turn the follower gear the same number of revolutions. The force is increased and the speed reduced. With a low gear ratio (the follower gear has fewer teeth), the driver gear has to turn less (less distance at the circumference) to turn the follower gear the same number of revolutions. This results in increased speed and reduced force.

When speaking of gears, force is commonly referred to as "torque," or rotational force.

Most people these days don't drive manual transmission cars. Even large trucks are beginning to use automatic transmissions, as they've become more and more efficient over the years. Still, even in many automatic transmissions, the option exists to shift down manually. Shifting down results in a higher gear ratio that makes the engine or drivetrain spin faster at a slower road speed. When going uphill, you move more slowly, but with more power. When going downhill, the engine and drivetrain movement itself slows the vehicle, helping to keep it under control. You have to be careful not to let the rotations per minute (rpm's) get too high—you do that by applying the brakes and slowing the car—or things might fly apart! Drivetrains flying apart can get expensive.

Another example, possibly more familiar to you, is a multi-speed bicycle, such as a 10- or 21-speed. If you haven't experienced it yourself, you've likely seen someone biking up a hill with their legs pumping furiously, but the bike is barely moving. They're in a high gear ratio, which lets them apply a lot of force at the expense of distance (moving their legs a bunch). Shifting up (to a lower gear ratio) when going downhill means their legs move less and their bicycle covers a lot of ground!

***Gear ratios and shifting up or down:*** Gearing up actually means using a lower gear ratio, and gearing down means using a higher gear ratio. Stated another way, when shifting in a manual transmission, we aren't thinking of moving gear ratios, we're thinking of going from 1st to 5th gear, for example. So indeed, we're shifting up and down. It's confusing when you think about what's happening with the gear ratios themselves. Now you know!

**Gear ratios on bikes**
https://www.youtube.com/watch?v=qacvtrh-ot8

## EXPERIMENTS: LET'S BUILD SOMETHING!

### Gears Experiment #1: Change of Direction

#### Parts Needed:

(Note, these are the parts needed for Gears Experiments 1 through 3):

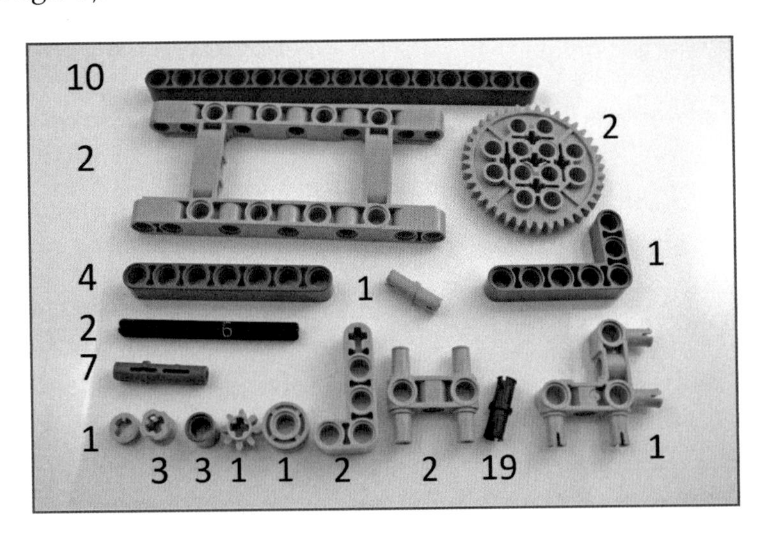


#### Procedures:

1. Build the gear tower

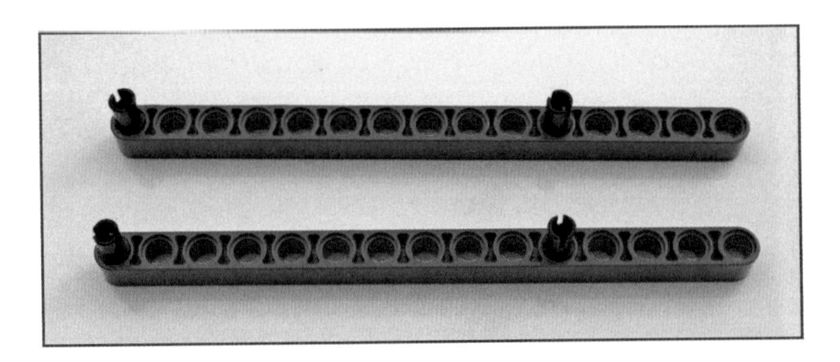

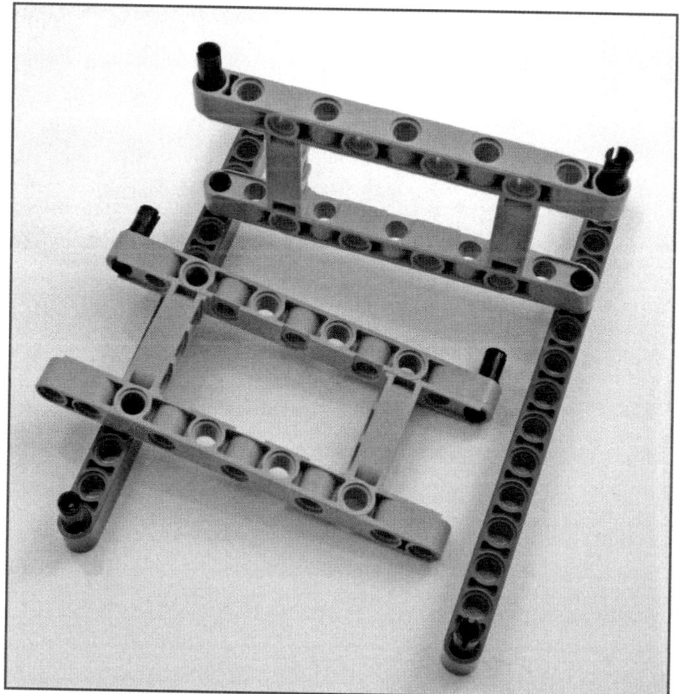

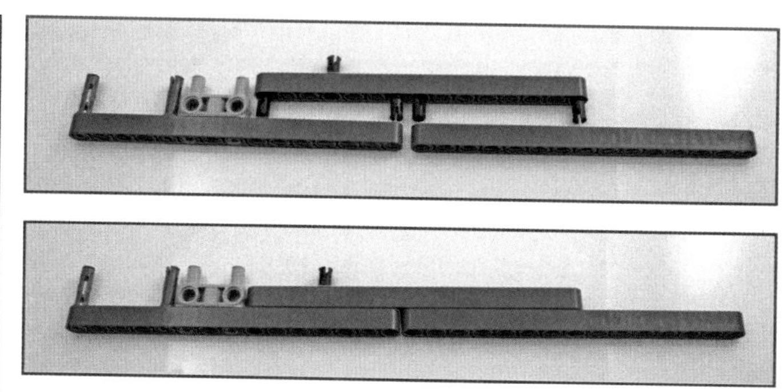

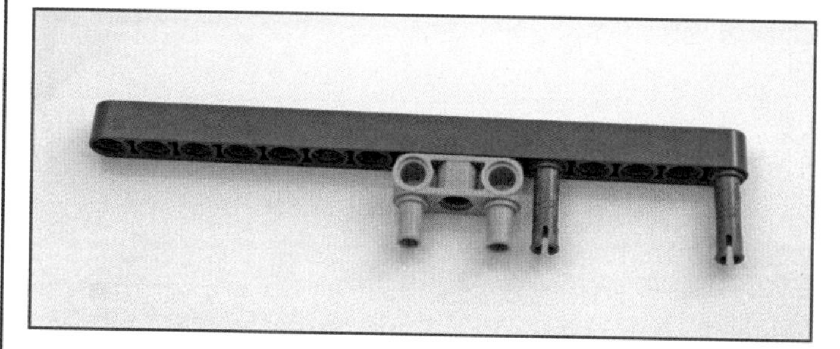

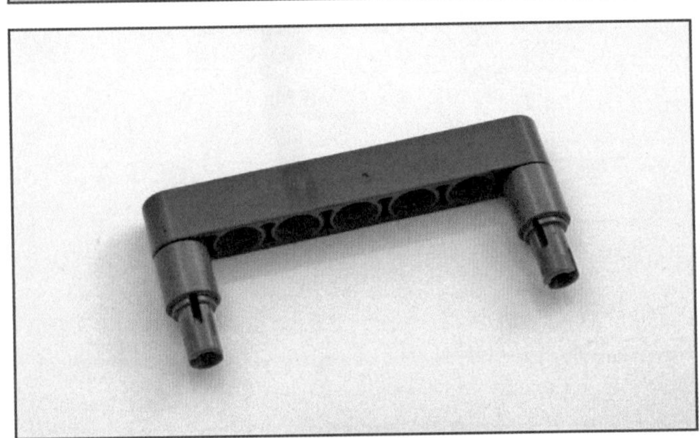

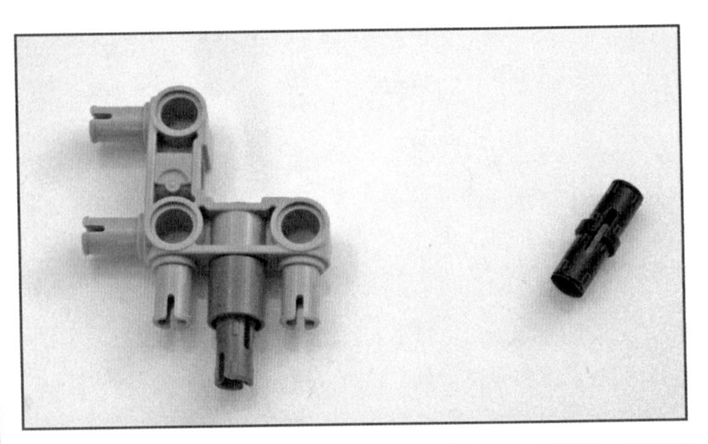

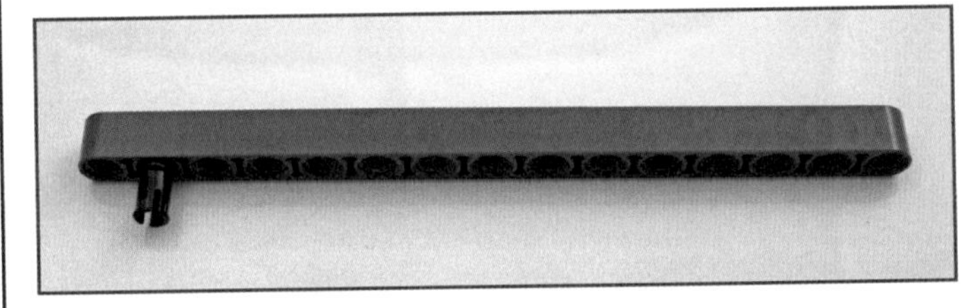

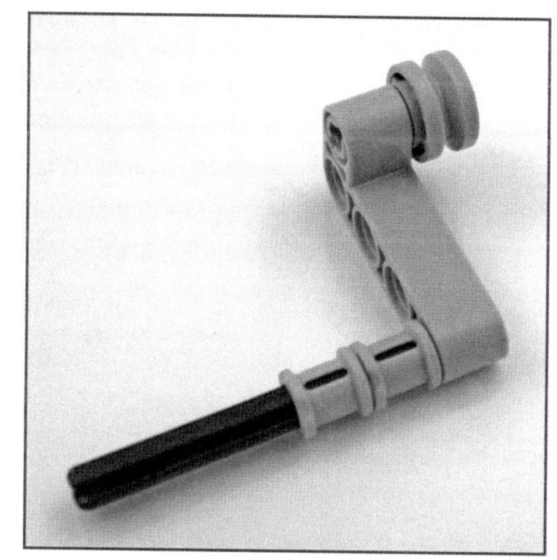

Note: Any rotational areas shouldn't be pinched by neighboring pieces. They need to rotate freely.

2. The 40-tooth gear should be on the bottom, as the driver gear on the crank assembly, and the 8-tooth gear as the follower gear on top, attached to the "windmill."
3. Hold your hand on the tower for stability and turn the crank.

4. Note how the crank and windmill rotational directions are reversed from one another.
5. Now remove the windmill assembly by removing the axle bushing, keeping the rest intact. Add a 24-tooth gear between the driver gear and the windmill gear.

6. Turn the crank and record your observations. Don't dismantle the windmill; you'll need it for Gears Experiment #2.

### Gears Experiment #1: Change of Direction Discussion

When engineers are designing a new machine, frequently the tool needs to turn in a particular direction but isn't directly attached to the driving force. For our windmill example, it could have been attached directly to the crank. Transferring energy through gears is one way to move the energy, and the number of gears determines the tool's rotational direction. Play around with this a bit, using the gears available to you. Use your imagination, taking careful note of how the gears turn, the speed each gear turns, and how all these things change as you rearrange the gears.

If you'd like to experiment with more types of gears, take a look at what's available at LEGO.com, specifically these two sites:

https://www.LEGO.com/en-us/service/replacementparts: This site lets you order unique bricks, or get replacement bricks for sets you already have. It can also be a good resource if you have lost pieces needed for this workbook.

https://shop.LEGO.com/en-us/page/static/pick-a-brick: This site lets you order many common bricks in sets currently for sale.

## Gears Experiment #2: Force and Speed Multiplication

### Procedures:

**Part 1**

1. Use same windmill setup as for Gears Experiment #1. Remove the middle follower gear and the windmill assembly, and then replace the windmill so that it engages the 40-tooth driver gear on the crank. The model should be back to where you started on Gears Experiment #1.

2. Note the speed at which the windmill turns and any resistance to turning the crank.

3. Calculate the mechanical advantage of turning the windmill using the crank. Record any observations.

**Part 2**

1. Switch the gear on the crank (driver) with the gear on the windmill (follower).

2. Turn the crank, noting again the speed at which the windmill turns and any resistance to turning the crank.
3. Calculate the mechanical advantage of turning the windmill using the crank. Record any observations.

## Gears Experiment #2: Force and Speed Multiplication Discussion

You should have noted a large difference in speed when you switched the gears. Also, more resistance exists when the larger gear is the driver. Force multiplication occurs when the small gear serves as the driver gear, resulting in reduced resistance to cranking. When switched, with the larger gear serving as the driver, speed multiplication occurs, with greater resistance to cranking. Remember, *Work = force x distance.*

Can you think of other instances of this type of arrangement? You may have realized that the windmill reference is actually reversed from real windmills. In the real world, windmills are powered by the wind, turning the gear attached to the windmill axle, the driver gear, and any that follow. The principles are the same. In fact, you can experiment by turning the windmill with your finger instead of turning the crank. Note what happens to the crank.

Windmills have been used for a long time to accomplish work, transferring energy to the points needed for grinding and milling grains, such as wheat, or turning saw blades. Force or speed multiplication was controlled by the proper combination of gears or, in some cases, large crank wheels with belts. In either case, the principles are the same.

## Gears Experiment #3: Another Windmill

Another, more common method of transferring energy is through gears on axles.

### Parts Needed:

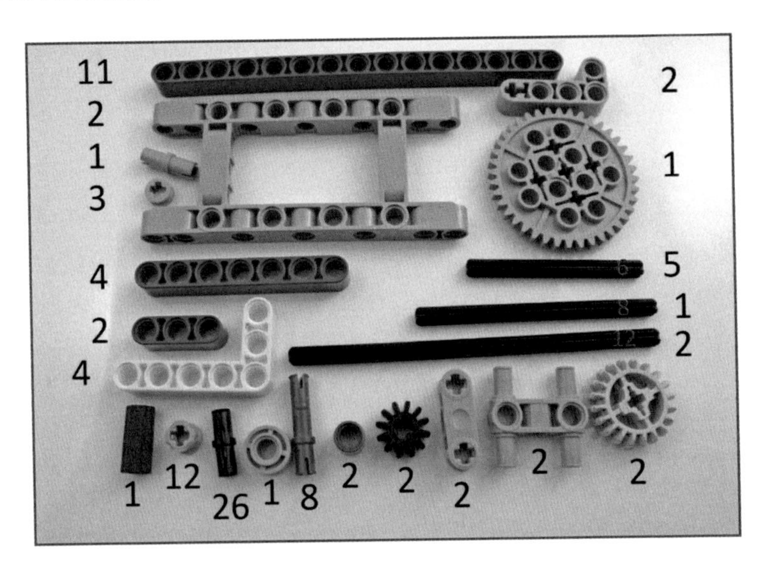


### Procedures:

1. Build the tower.

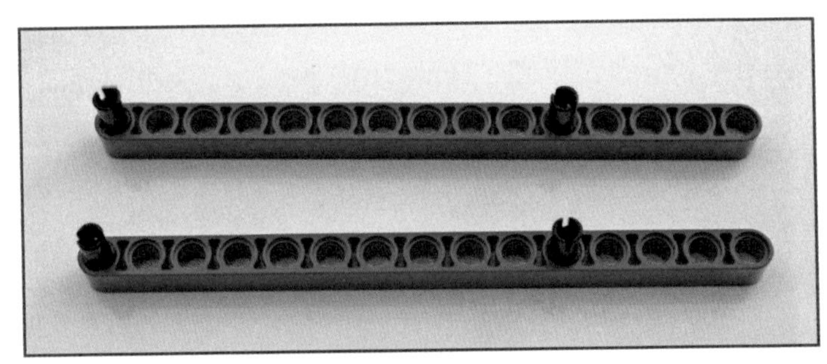

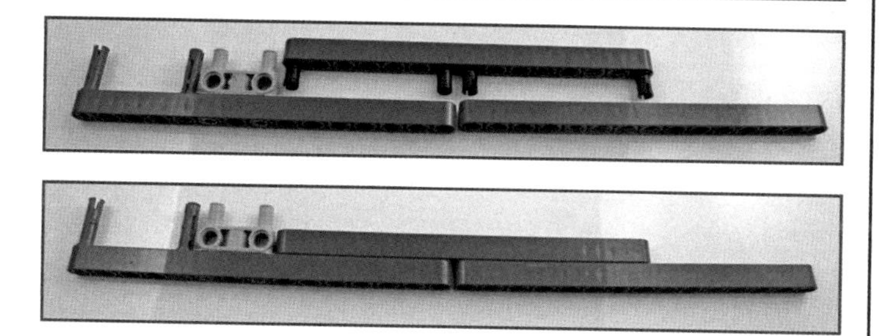

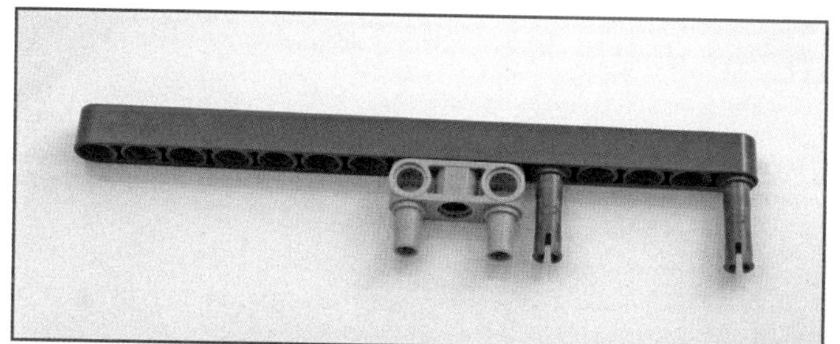

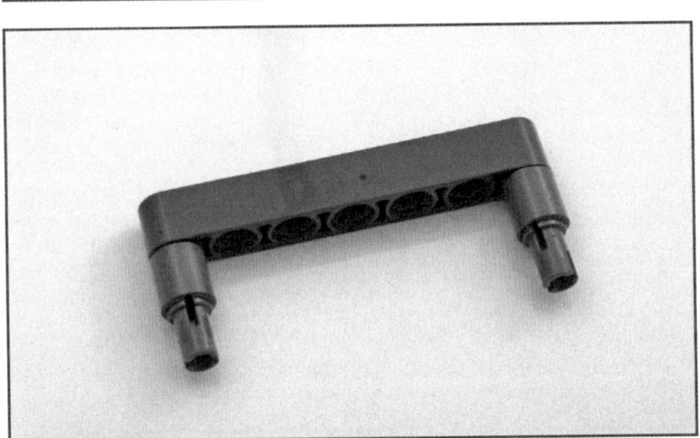

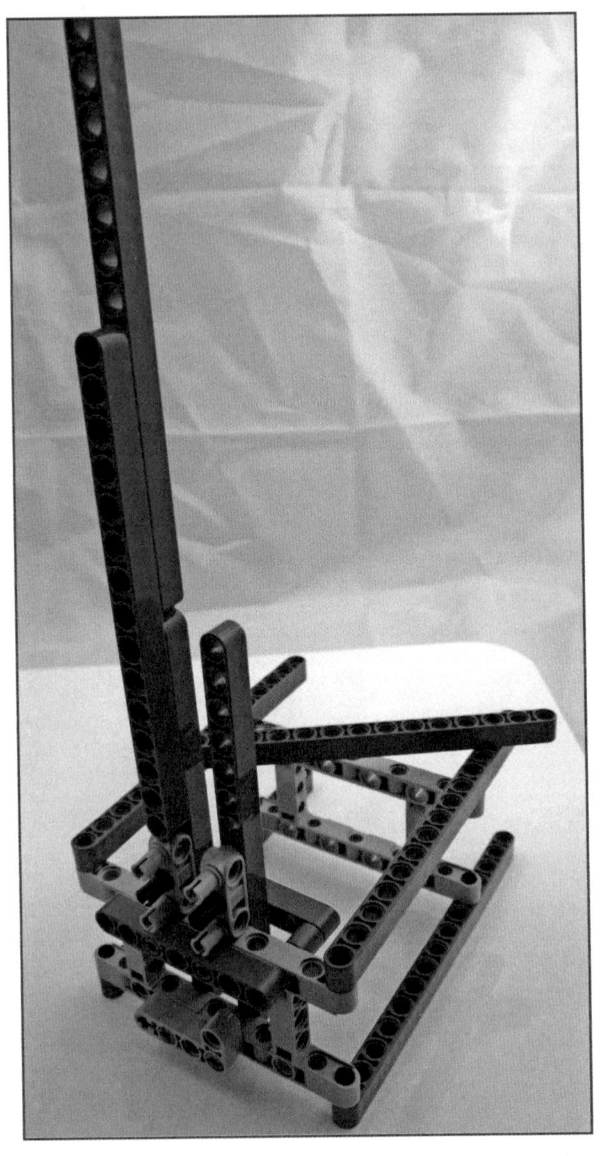

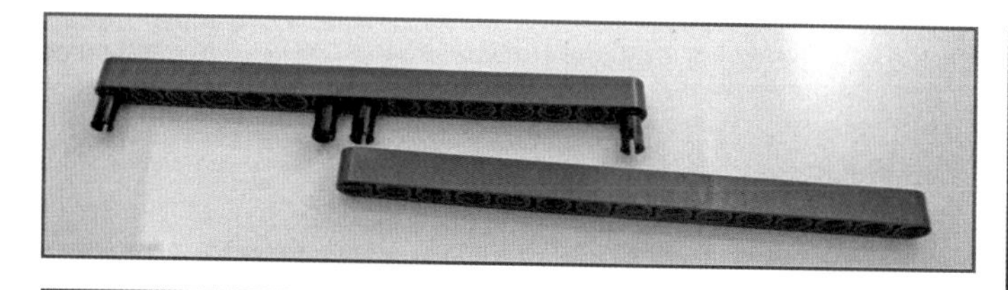

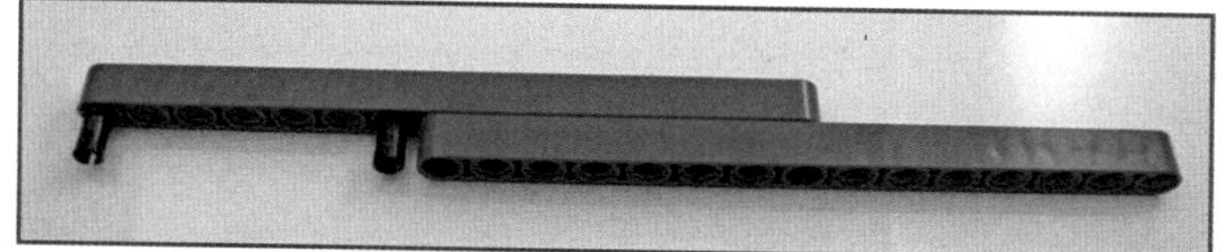

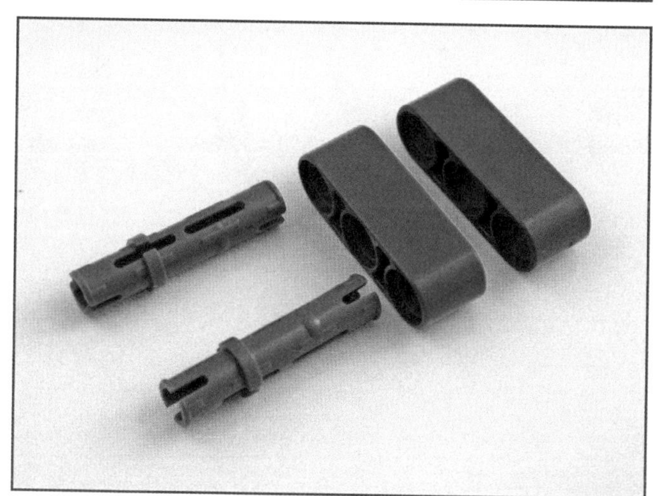

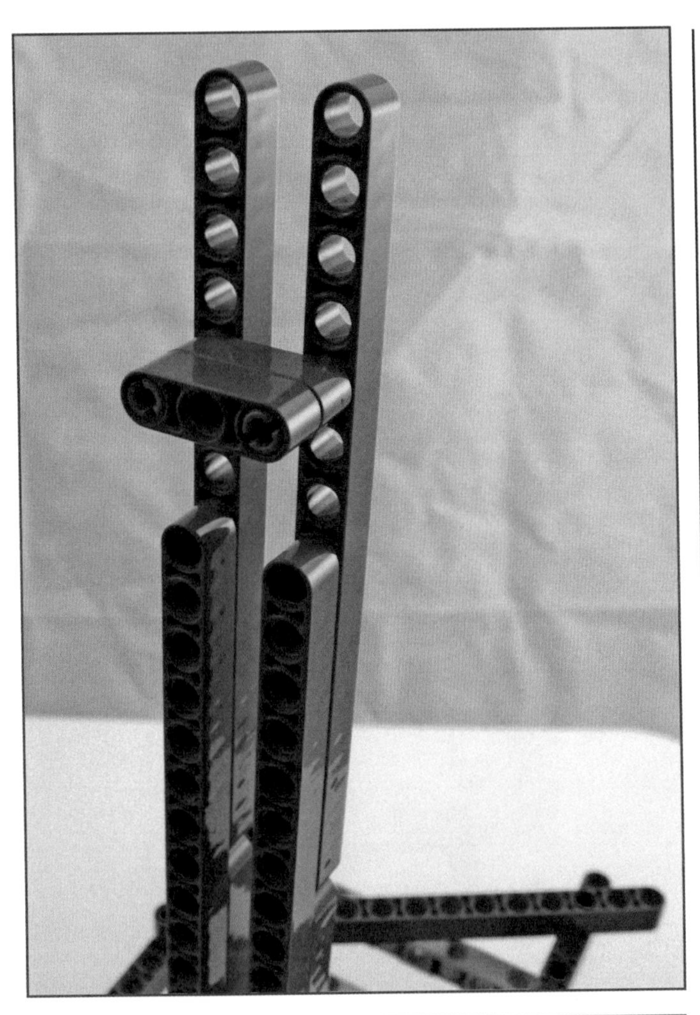

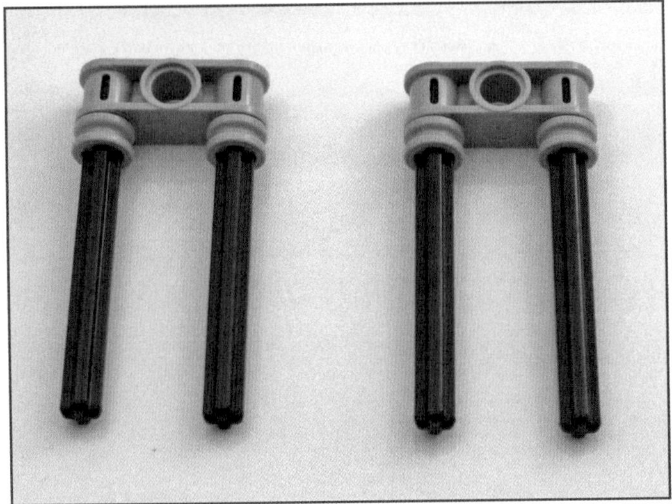

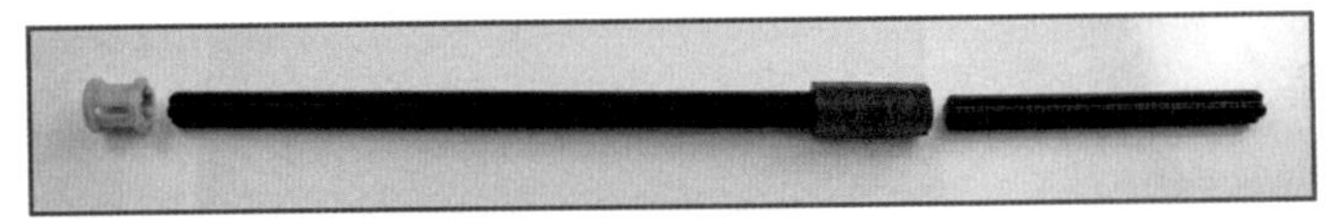

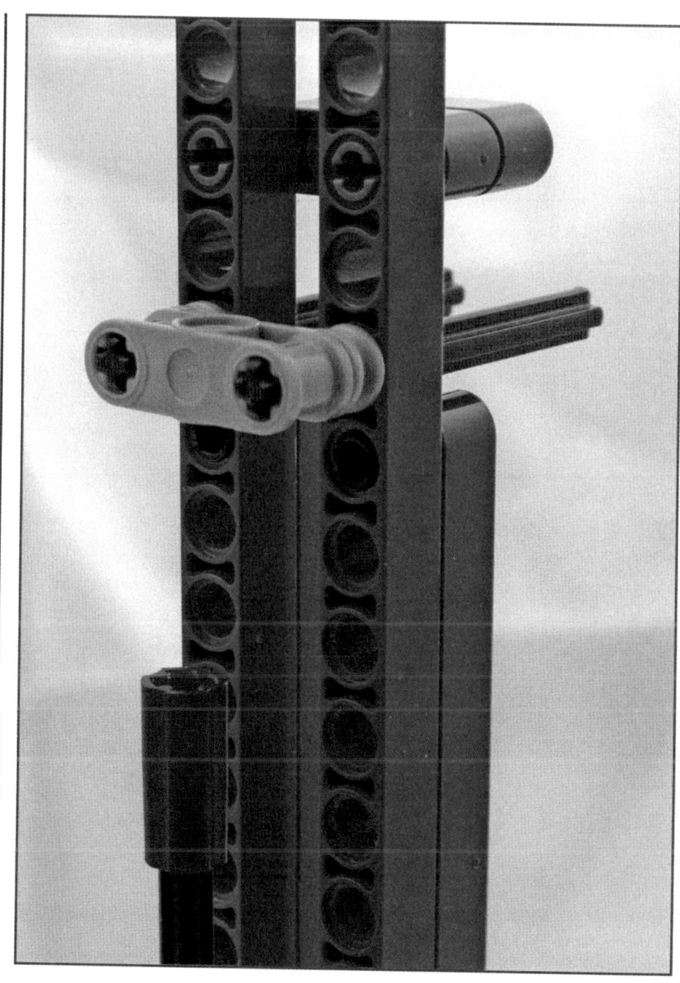

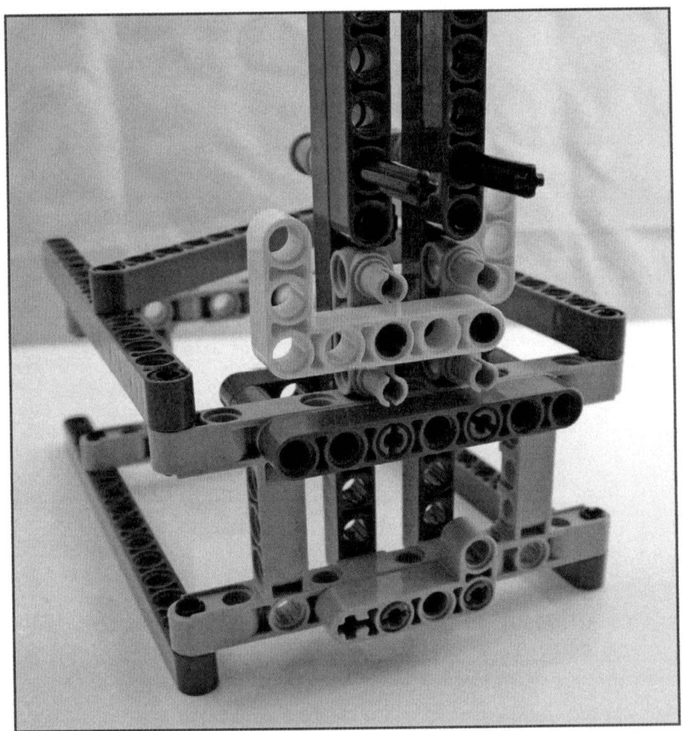

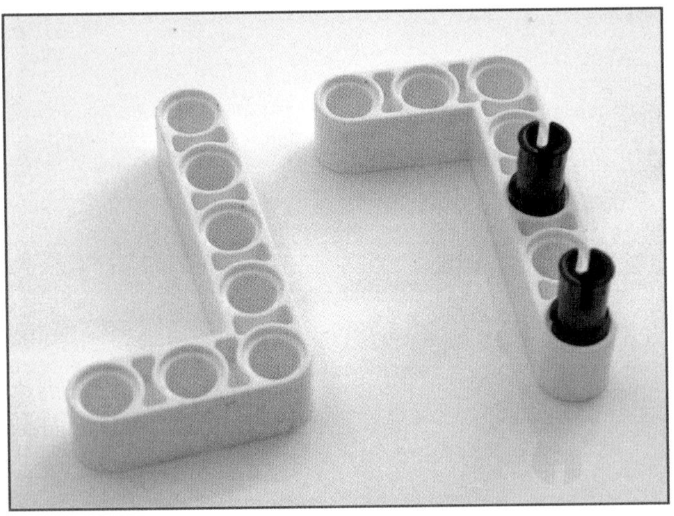

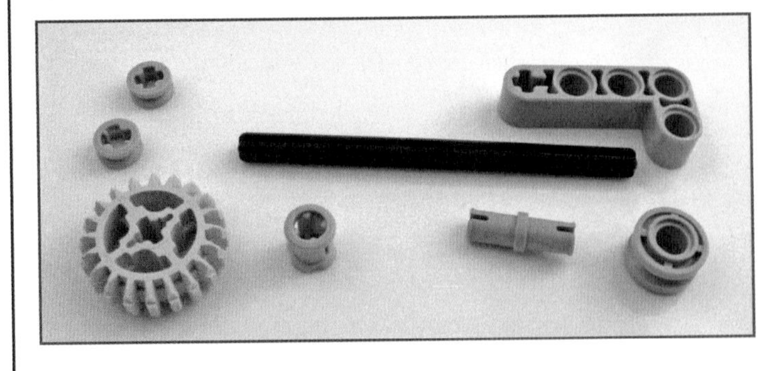

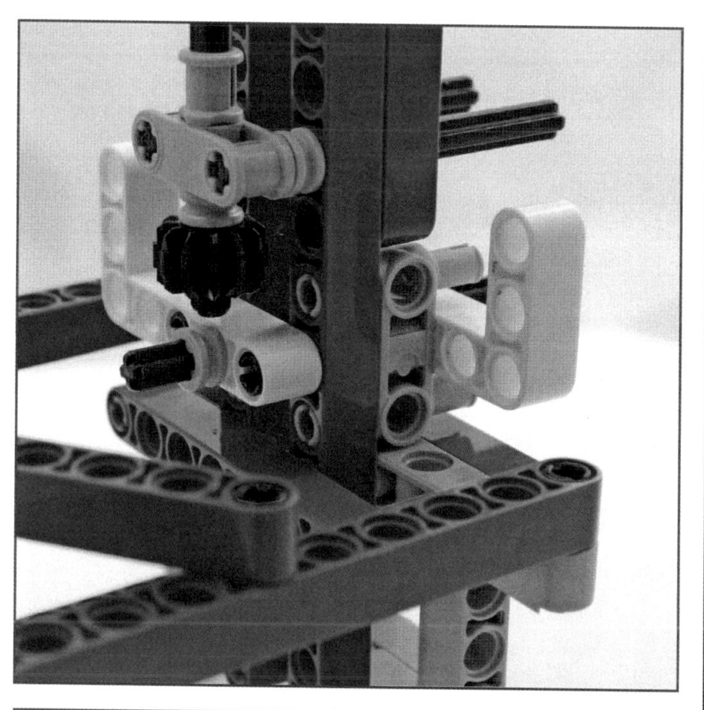

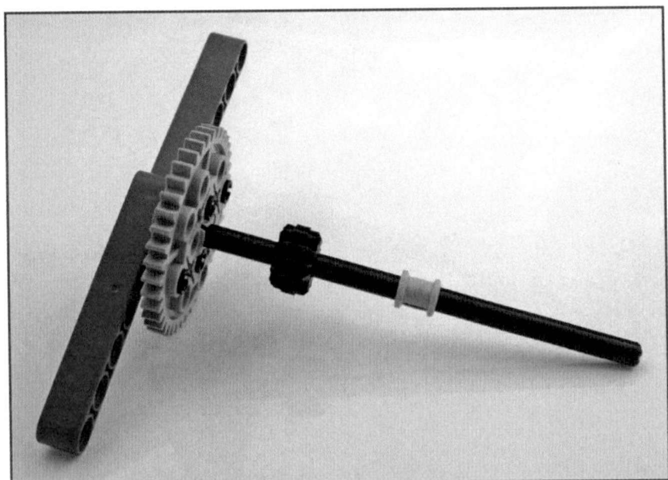

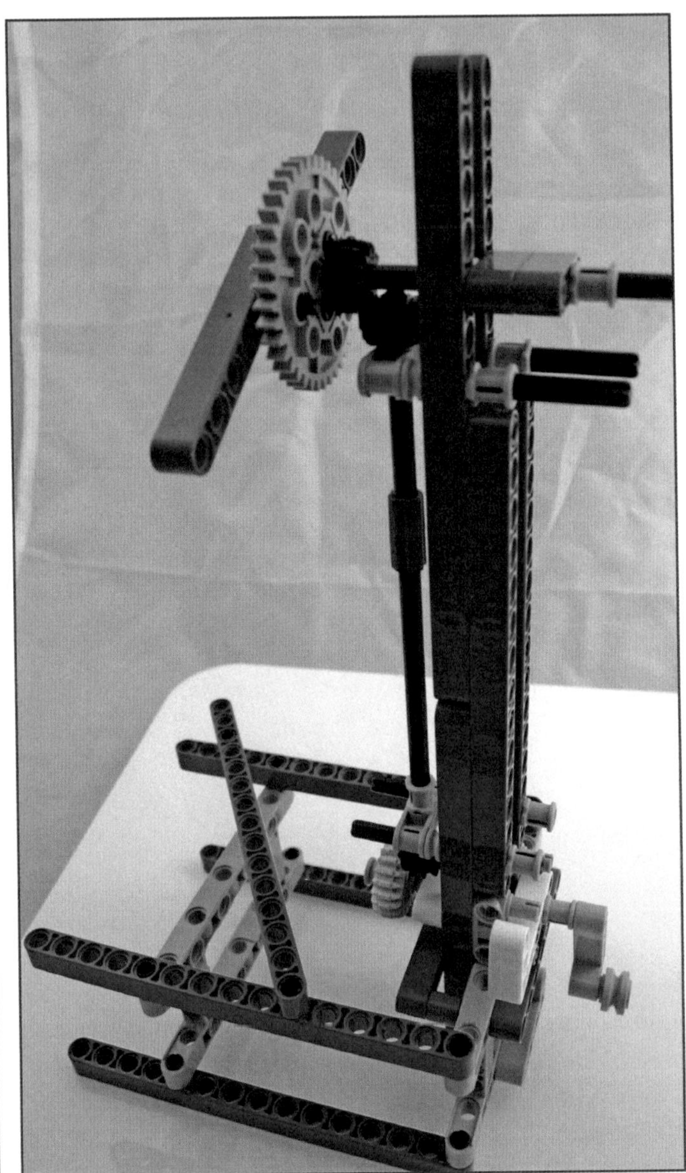

2. Rotate the crank and note the windmill blade speed.
3. Rebuild and remodel the vertical axle to allow for the larger tan-colored gears.

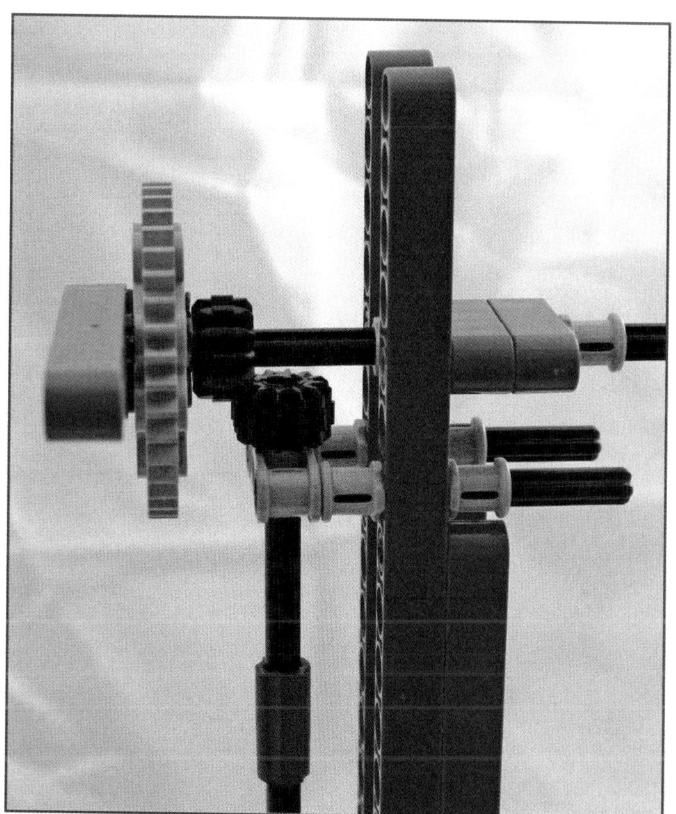

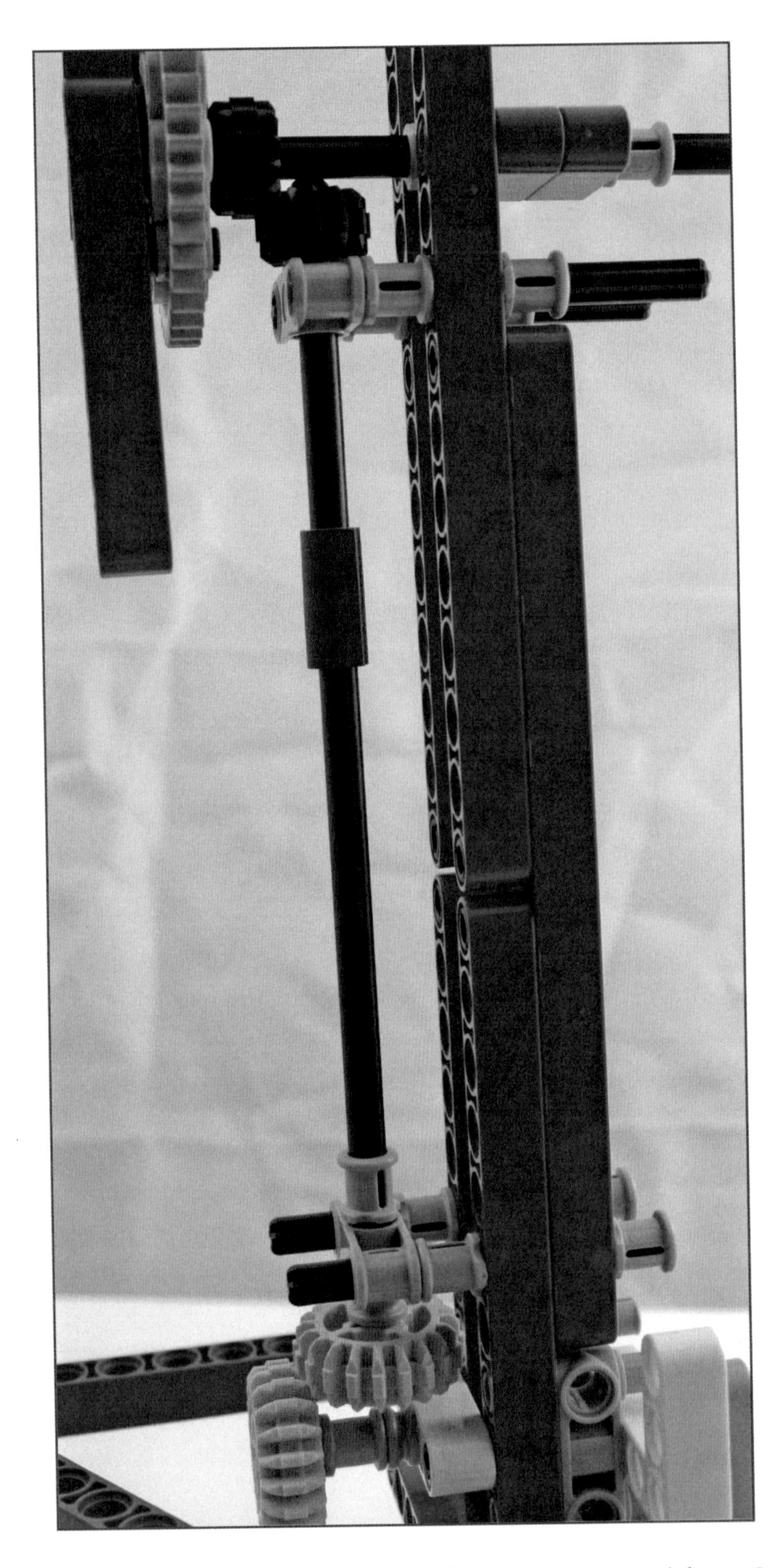

4. Turn the crank, noting any difference in speed from Step 2. Record your observations.

### Gears Experiment #3: Another Windmill Discussion

This configuration is simpler than having a large row of rotating gears. Every intermeshing gear would require regular maintenance and grease to avoid excessive and premature wear. With a single axle and only two gears, energy can be transferred a long distance with a relatively small number of moving parts, and therefore relatively low maintenance.

## Gears Experiment #4: Screw Gears

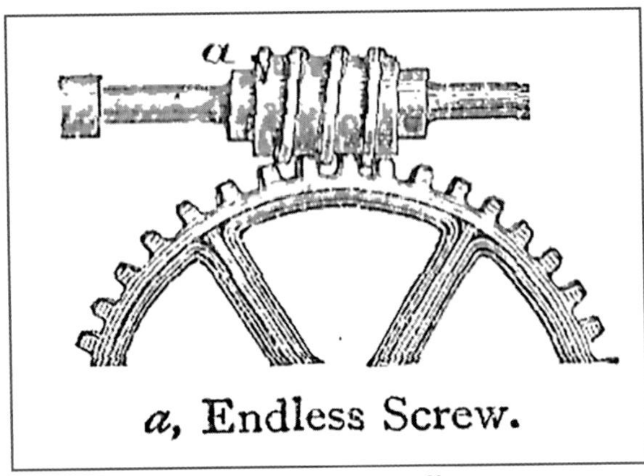


An endless screw[29]

An interesting type of gear is the screw gear—simplistically, a rotating inclined plane intermeshed with a traditional toothed gear. Let's try out one variation.

### Parts Needed:

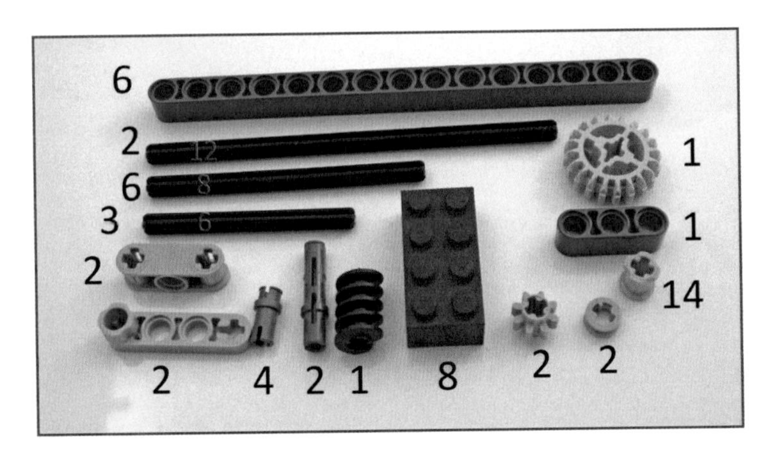


### Procedures

1. Build the model. Don't confuse the gear on the axle end with a functional gear. It's here solely as a knob to make turning the axle easier.

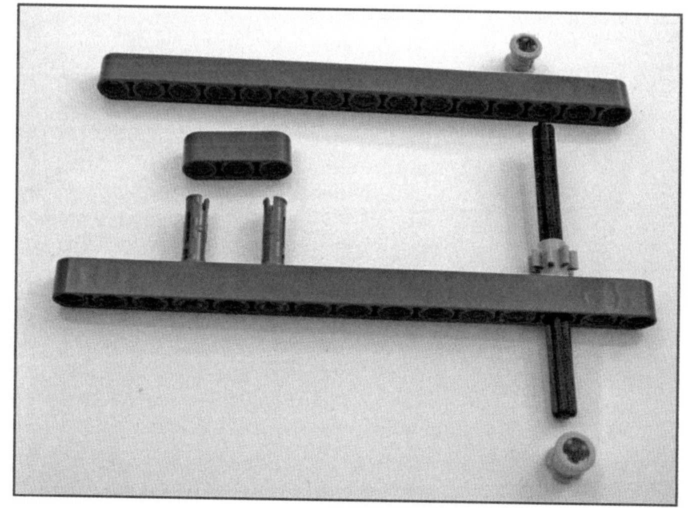

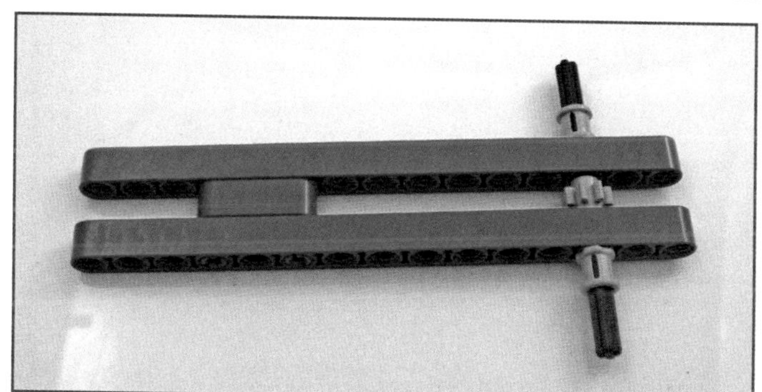

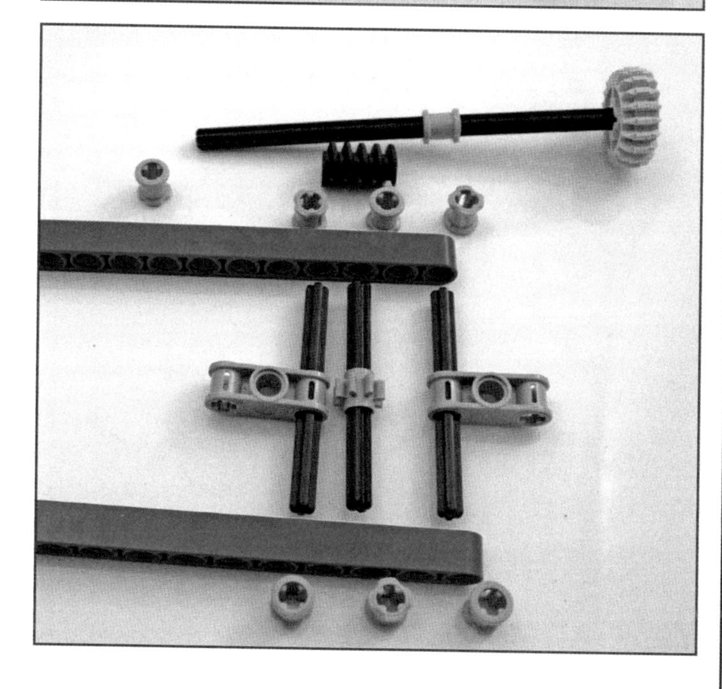

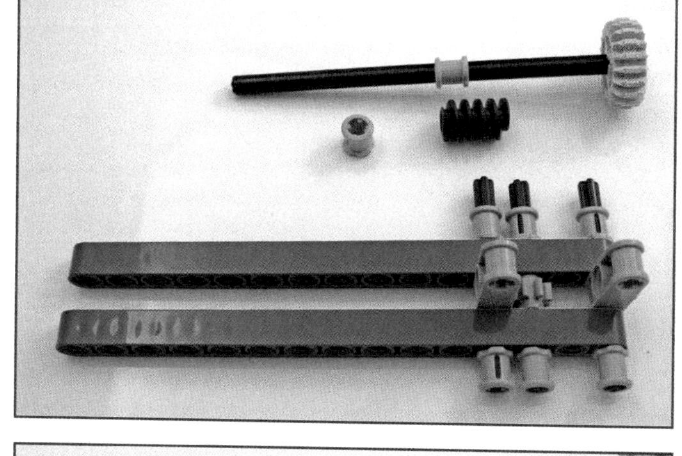

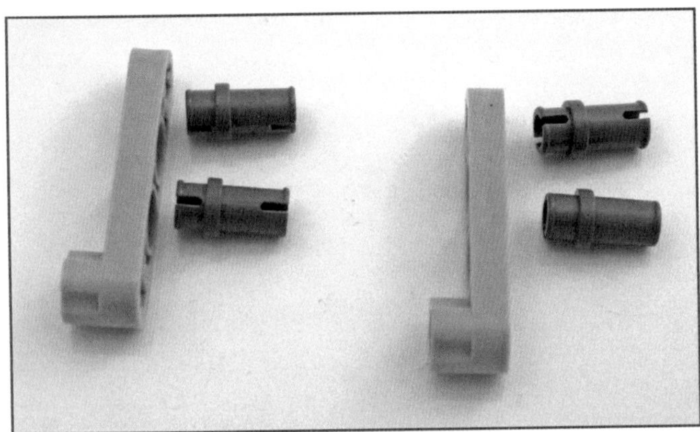

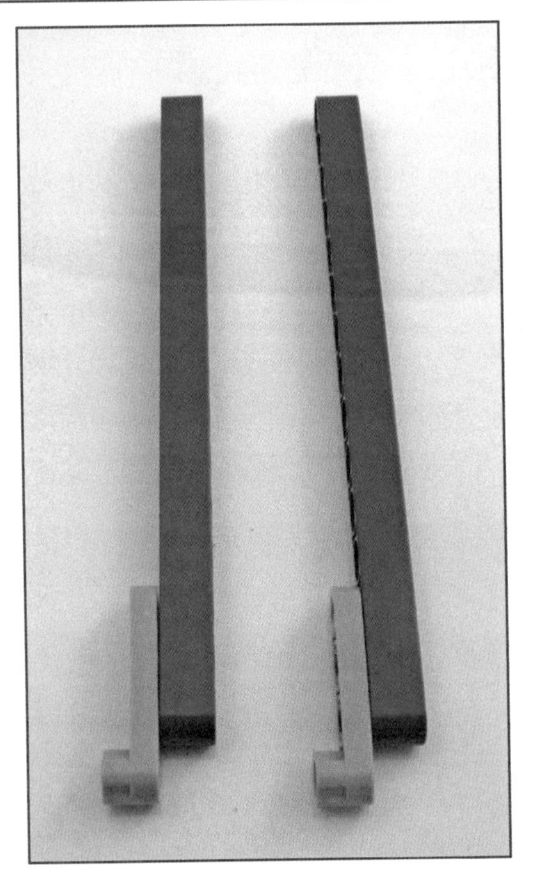

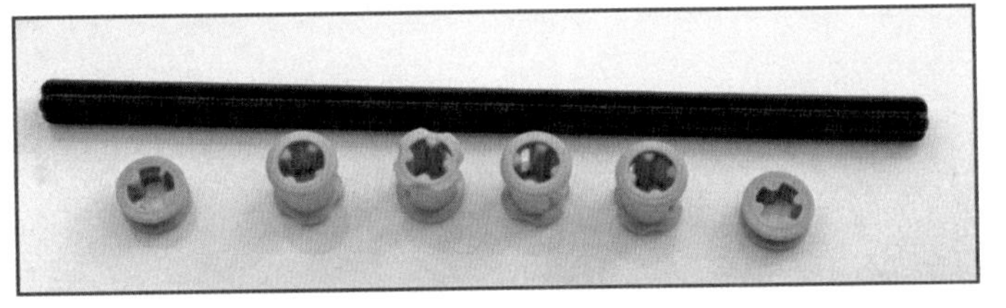

2. Turn the axle and note what happens. Observe how high it can go, and any "slop" or play in the mechanism.

3. Turn the axle all the way back, and all the way forward. Record your observations. Have you seen examples of this type of machine?

***Slop or play:*** When describing mechanical systems, these terms refer to looseness in the mechanism. For example, toothed gears might not be tight against one another due to wear or improper fit. However, the opposite, being too tight, can also be a problem as you've surely seen when building the models throughout this workbook.

## Gears Experiment #4: Screw Gears Discussion

The screw gear intermeshed with a normal toothed gear is a common machine mechanism. Drawbridges—or bridges that rotate up and down to allow for tall objects to move through, such as over a waterway—are sometimes assembled this way. It's a controlled, smooth, continuous motion. Drills and many hand-powered tools, such as mixers, have screw gears. I own a travel trailer with a powered awning that uses a screw gear variation which has become quite common. It's a screw gear wrapped by another screw gear attached to a fixed object. The internal screw gear in this case is long and rotates, moving the external one along the long shaft. Whatever is attached to the external wraparound gear moves along the shaft.

## Gears Experiment #5: The Rack and Pinion

The rack and pinion assembly is another common machine used all over the world in many different applications. One common function is for turning car wheels; another is for lifting flat objects vertically, such as a gate.

**This video explains power steering, including hydraulics, in a rack and pinion steering mechanism.**
https://www.youtube.com/watch?v=Z1Y14AejfQU

The rack & pinion[30]

Another rack and pinion variation has the rack (the toothed portion in strip form) curved. The result is that as the pinion turns, the curved rack moves with the same degree of rotation. This modification has also been used for drawbridges, among other things.

**Parts Needed:**

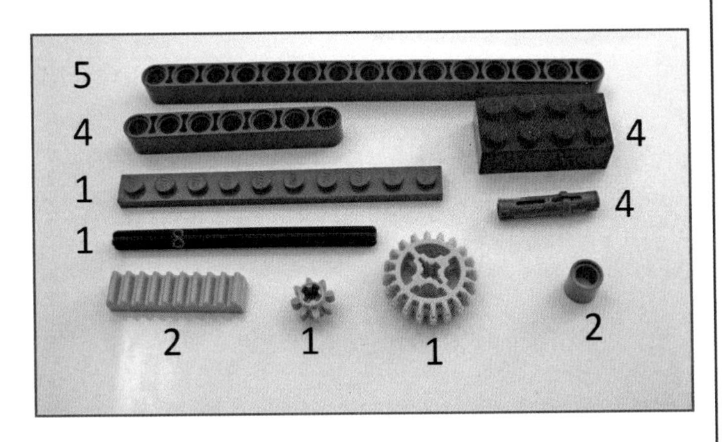


**Procedures:**

1. Build the rack and pinion model.

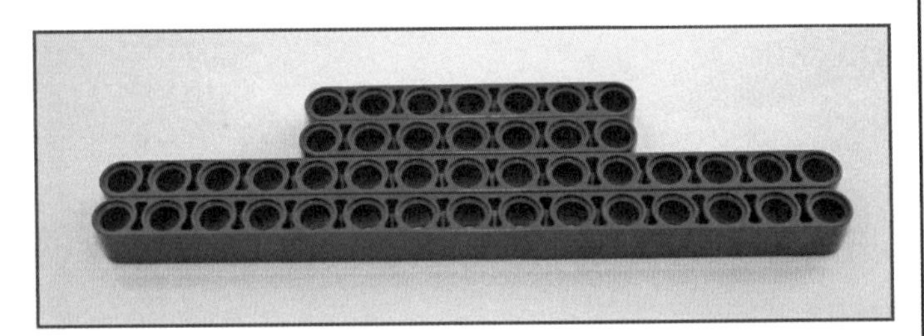

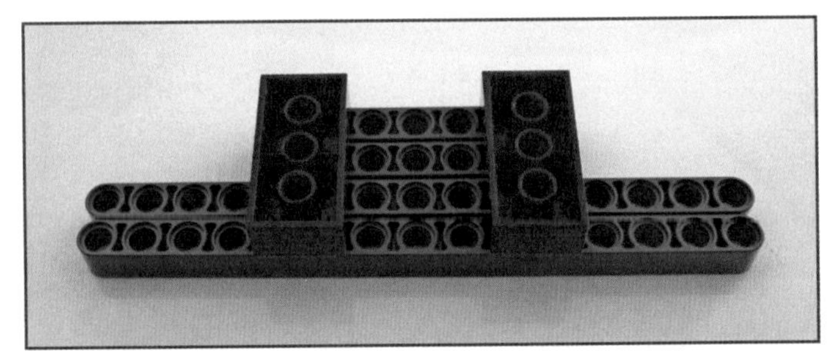

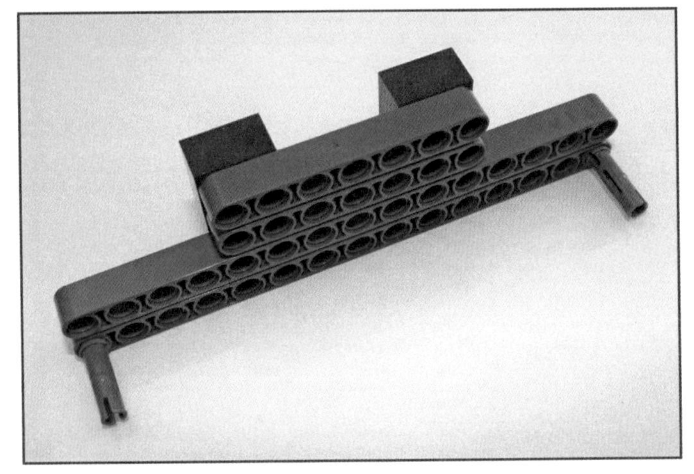

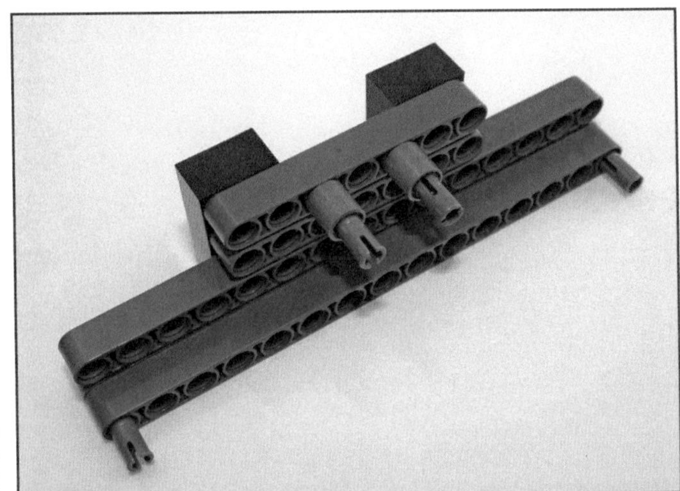

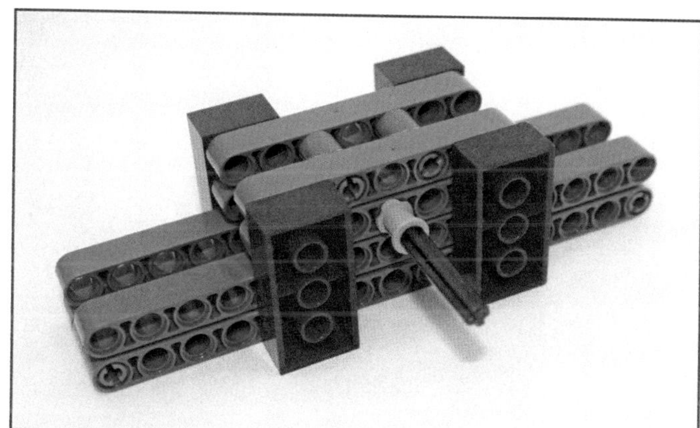

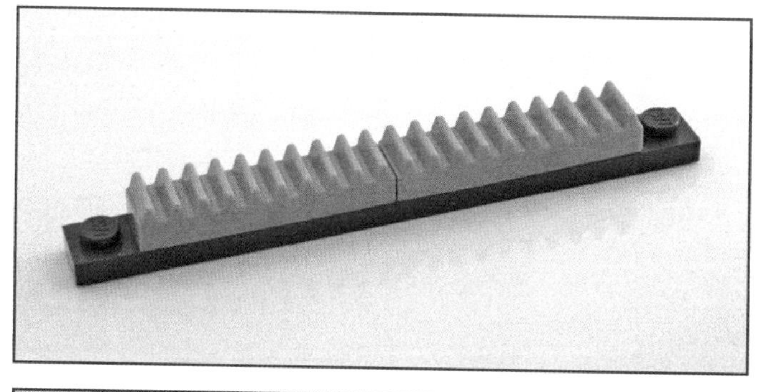

2. Turn the pinion back and forth. Record any observations.

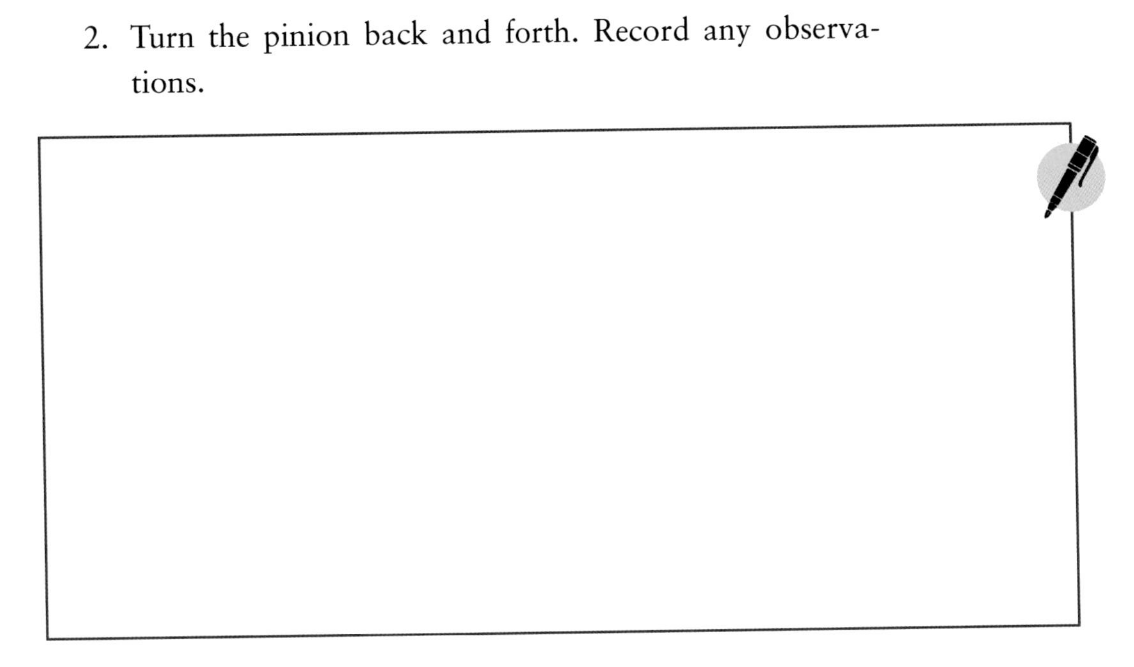

## Gears Experiment #5: The Rack and Pinion Discussion

Can you think of a way to modify this model to increase the rack's speed? Based on what you learned about multiplying speed earlier in the book, what do you think will happen if you increase the pinion gear's diameter? While I was developing this model for the workbook, one alternative had the largest diameter gear in the set. The result was that a quick turn of the pinion gear would result in the rack shooting out the end like an arrow. Try it! You can modify your model in of lots ways. Use your imagination!

## Gears Experiment #6: Universal Joints

You've seen pictures of universal joints, now let's try some.

### Parts Needed:

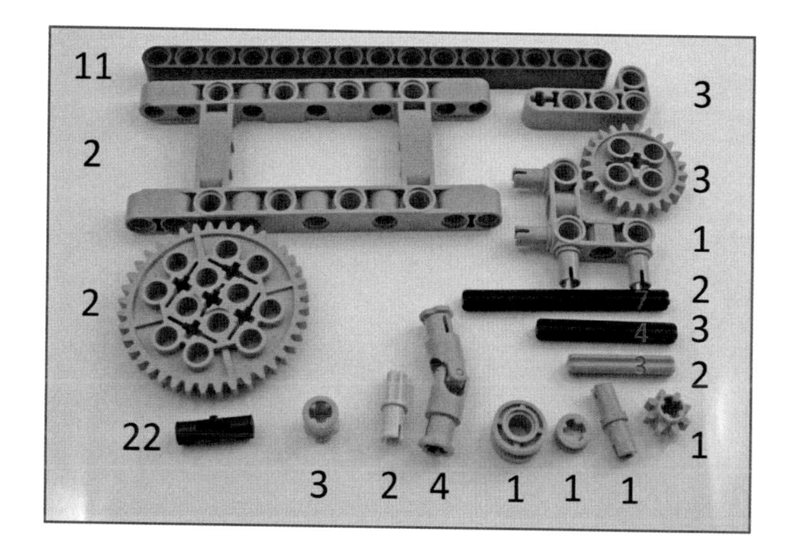


### Procedures:

1. Build the machine.

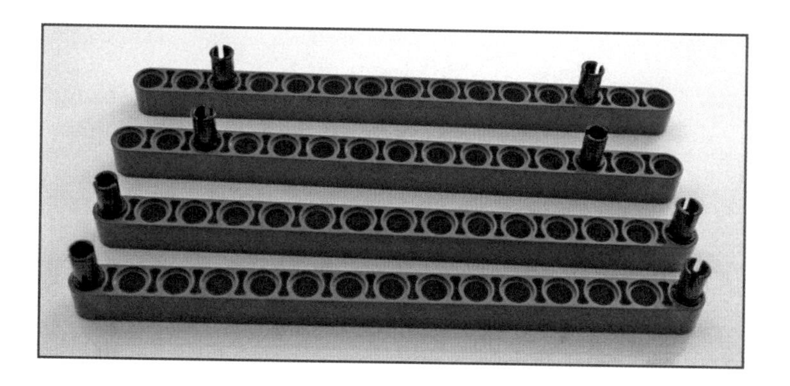

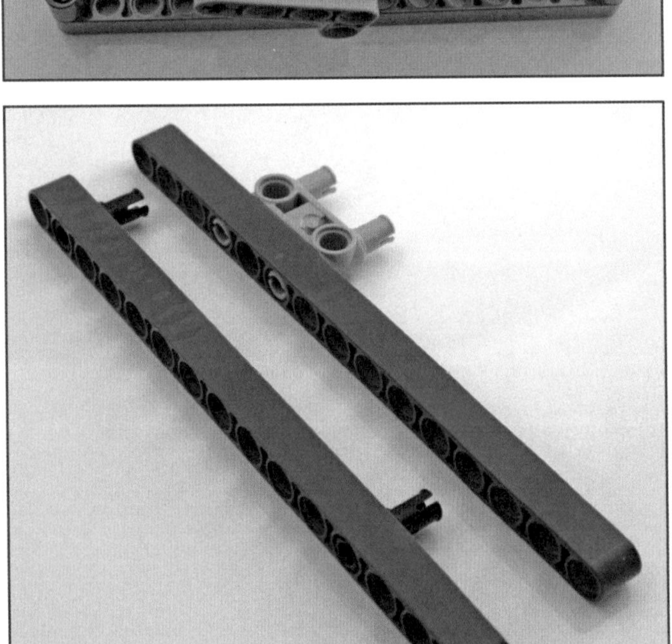

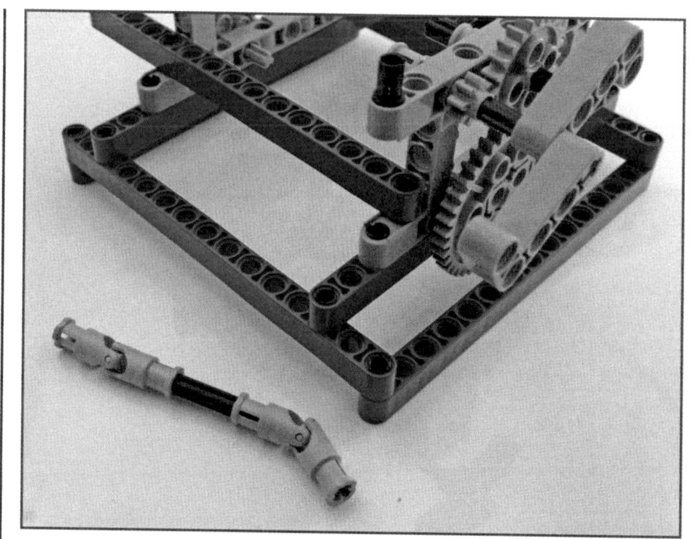

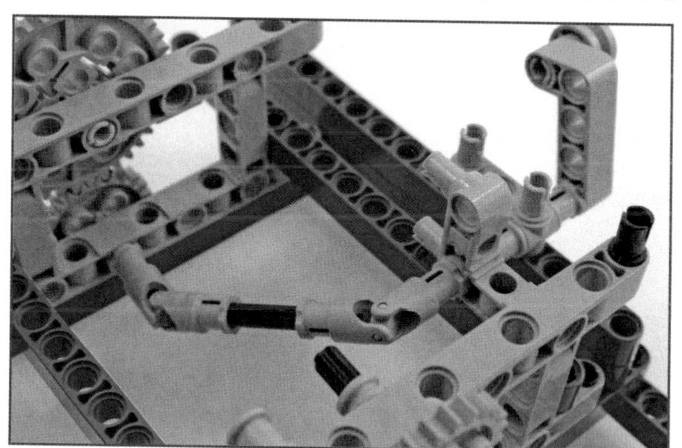

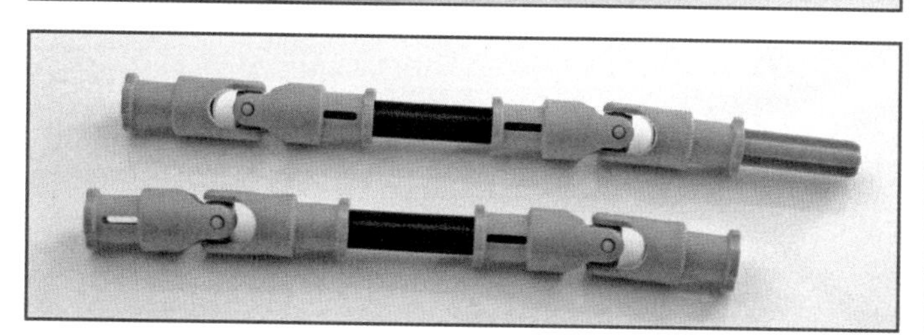

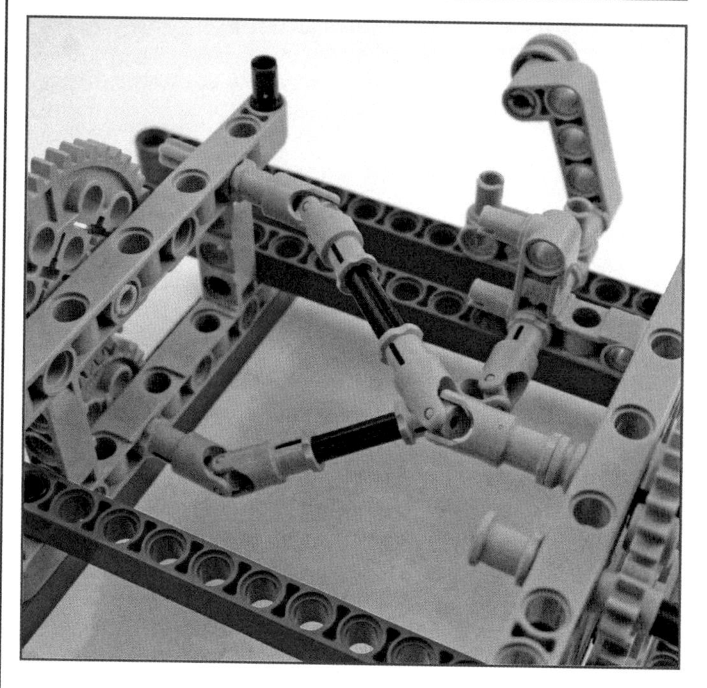

2. Make sure that all the rotating parts aren't pinching any stationary parts.
3. Turn the crank very slowly. Note how the "propeller" moves, whether smoothly or in a jerking fashion.

4. Now turn the crank quickly, noting again the behavior of the propeller. Can you think of why the behavior is different? Record your observations.

### Gears Experiment #6: Universal Joints Discussion

This was a machine designed to demonstrate the transfer of power through universal joints and gears. Universal joints and gears are pretty cool and allow for the transfer of energy efficiently from one point to another, even over long distances and changing direction multiple times if needed. If you observed closely, you'll have noticed that the universal joint closest to the crank was the primary cause of the slop or jerkiness experienced when turning the crank at high speeds. Universal joints work well with modest changes in direction. This particular change in the angle was more drastic than is likely recommended for smooth operation—at least for this universal joint.

## WHAT DO YOU THINK?

Gears are interesting, and you can assemble them in endless options! Again, while researching this book, I reviewed some old books and was impressed with the ingenuity used to create complex gear mechanisms designed to make tasks easier back when there weren't powerful electric motors available. You should check them out—it's cool stuff!

## JOURNALING IDEA

Imagine you're a new engineer working for a new space exploration company and have been tasked with designing a ring system for the habitat module to be assembled in Earth orbit, then used to take explorers to a neighboring star system. This ring system needs to spin to mimic gravity for the explorers. You want to minimize weight, so you can't put a large motor in to spin the ring system. How would you design the gear system?

## CHAPTER REVIEW

1. You're riding your 10-speed bike along a nice and level path when you approach and start going up a hill. Do

you want to change to a higher or lower gear ratio? Explain.

2. A drive shaft on a breakfast cereal packaging machine is constantly breaking because one end frequently moves a little bit. As the engineer supporting the line, what would you recommend to solve the problem?
3. Take a drive to a local construction site. Park in a safe location and count up all the hydraulic cylinders you can see. Bring along some binoculars if you have them.
4. In the previous question, you saw large diameter cylinders and smaller ones. Why are larger diameter cylinders needed? How does that work?
5. Have you ever heard of gears being "stripped?" This means that some gear teeth have come off or been ground down, allowing them to slip past each other rather than smoothly and consistently transferring power. How can this happen? If you know a mechanic, you should ask them. They'd know quite a lot about the problem, and you would find the conversation interesting.

# CONCLUSION

I hope you've enjoyed this workbook. The laws of physics applied to machines really do make life easier, as I hope you were able to see through the many experiments and the concepts associated with them. As I write this, I'm in my early 50s, and I still collect LEGO® sets! I love to build the LEGO® Technic™ models to see how things work.

A few notes are in order as we conclude this workbook.

## MACHINE MAINTENANCE

All machines require regular maintenance. My own previously mentioned track loader has had several breakdowns, and the repairs can be expensive. I've come to realize that these repairs are part of working with powerful machines that greatly magnify force and movement. For example, one of the main hydraulic cylinders developed a severe leak and had to be repaired. It's a somewhat difficult process, and if you'd like to see it, it's on my YouTube channel, here: https://www.youtube.com/channel/UCHARWGW8pLJeIau50fMHbxA?view_as=subscriber. Or, search for "Dale W Cox" on YouTube!

Even simple machines require maintenance. Perhaps the simplest example is making sure a ramp isn't slippery. Another is a screwdriver losing its "bite" when the part that fits into the screw becomes deformed. This can happen when tools are mistreated—in this case, using the screwdriver to scrape or chisel materials, eventually filing away the tip and causing it to become nonfunctional for its intended purpose.

I was impressed with a man I hired to fix my track loader for an electrical issue I couldn't solve. He came with a truck loaded with about $250,000 worth of tools. (Remember, a tool is a simple or complex machine!) I watched as he carefully used each tool, then set them aside. When he was finished, he thoroughly cleaned and inspected each tool before putting them back where they belonged. I was inspired to treat my tools better.

## ENGINEERING

I hope that you also gained greater respect for the ingenuity that goes into all the devices we use every day. Engineers are amazing people, using their minds and understanding of the world around us (including physics!) to build things to help us accomplish what we want to do more efficiently.

Sometimes we need engineers to be able to accomplish a task at all. For example, we can easily dig a large hole with a track loader. Given enough time, we could also do it with a shovel, which still needs an engineered tool! However, we could never get to the moon, walk on it, and then get back to Earth again without a complex machine. That task requires some pretty intense and ingenious engineering.

## PHYSICS

Like all science, physics laws describe and define our understanding of the world around us through scientific testing and observation. It's important to remember that all science is never settled. Speaking as a scientist, I've never understood it when I hear the term "settled science," as I know there is no such thing. Our understanding is based on our limited knowledge, which is always subject to change tomorrow, or the next day, when new data becomes available. In my opinion, the term *laws* when applied to science need to be in quotes ("laws"). You should at least understand that's how scientists view them.

Having said that, some of our understandings are pretty good. Good enough, in fact, to allow engineers to build great machines that really work, allowing mankind to accomplish amazing things!

## CONTACT INFORMATION

Email: info@dalewcox.com

www.beakersandbricks.com

www.dalewcox.com

Address: Beakers & Bricks, LLC
PO Box 1014
Asheboro, North Carolina 27204
USA

Now that you've had a taste of physics and engineering, how about a taste of food science?

# FOOD SCIENCE EXPERIMENT: LET'S MAKE A MESS!

Finally—your food science experiment! It's wildly different from the rest of this workbook, but still required because this is an Edible Knowledge publication. Also, I unashamedly hope that you try this experiment, find it interesting, and decide to look for my Introduction to Food Science workbooks, available at *www.beakersandbricks.com*. Many more fun and interesting experiments and knowledge, even Edible Knowledge, is available in them. I hope you enjoy this experiment!

## FUN WITH GELATIN AND ENZYMES

### Background:

Enzymes are proteins found in all natural organisms, including ourselves and the vegetables we purchase. They're critical for accomplishing metabolic processes and, in turn, allowing life to continue. Having said that, enzymes must be accounted for when preparing food or you could end up with some unexpected results. Sometimes the results are good; other times... not so much. In this experiment, you see the direct effect of an enzyme on a finished food.

### Items needed:

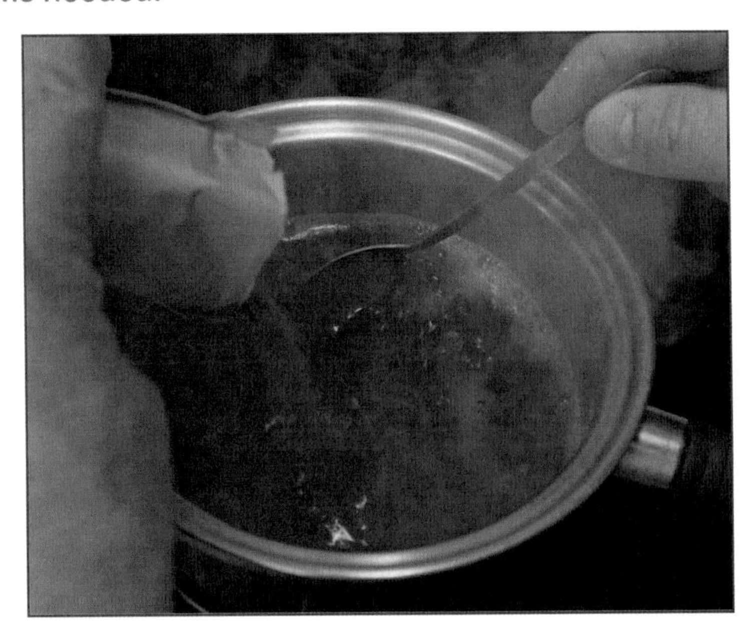

- One large box of gelatin dessert, any flavor (except not sugar-free)
- 1/4 cup diced fresh pineapple
- 1/4 cup diced canned pineapple
- Medium saucepan
- Two containers, preferably clear, that each holds about 2 cups of liquid. These containers will transfer the prepared gelatin to the refrigerator.
- Painter's or masking tape and a marker
- Cutting board
- Small knife (not serrated)

### Procedures:

1. Mark one container "fresh" and the other "canned" by using the tape and marker.
2. Cut the canned pineapple FIRST (before the fresh pineapple) on the cutting board into approximate 1/4" x 1/4" pieces, enough for about 1/4 cup. Add them to the container marked "canned."

> ***Note:*** It's important not to mix the fresh pineapple with the canned pineapple in any way!

3. Cut the fresh pineapple into 1/4" x 1/4" pieces. Add them to the container marked "fresh."
4. Prepare the gelatin in the saucepan, per the instructions, making sure to bring the gelatin and water to a complete boil and to eliminate all the gelatin granules.

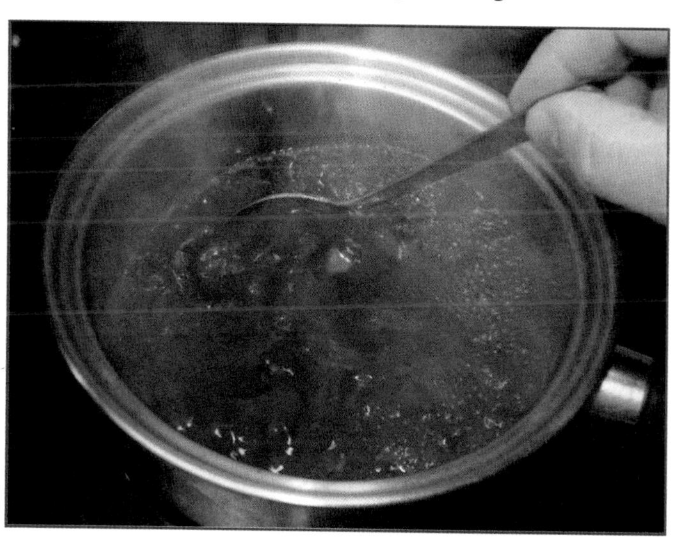

5. Add about half of the prepared gelatin to each container and stir for about 1 minute each. DO NOT use the same spoon to stir both containers.

6. Place in the refrigerator on a level surface and let chill for at least 12 hours.
7. Remove the containers from the refrigerator and record your observations.

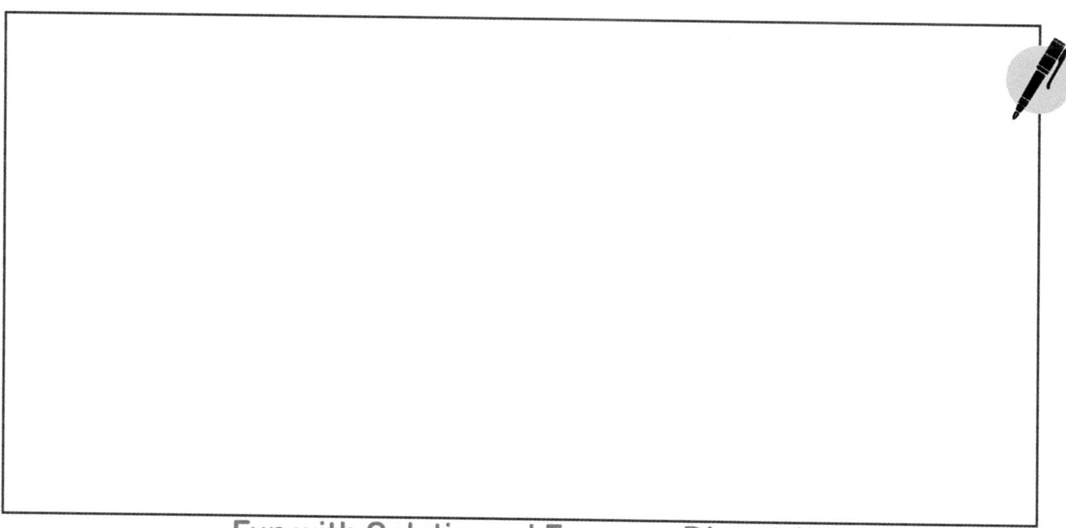

## Fun with Gelatin and Enzymes Discussion

You should have noticed that the gelatin in the container marked "fresh" didn't set up, or gel, at all, while the gelatin with the canned pineapple set up nicely. If it didn't, it's because the fresh pineapple, or its juice, became mixed with the canned.

Fresh pineapple contains enzymes that are natural proteases, meaning they cut up protein strands into smaller pieces. In fact, they're such good proteases that they're used in meat tenderizers that you can sprinkle on a tough cut of meat. Meat is a protein, and these tenderizers cleave the protein strands, making it less tough.

In our case, the enzymes were active in the fresh pineapple. Gelatin is a protein, and just like for tough meat, the pineapple proteases cut up the strands. Unfortunately for our intention of having a nice gelled dessert, we end up with pineapple soup instead.

So why didn't it happen with the canned pineapple? The reason is enzymes, while amazing molecules, are highly susceptible to damage from heat. Canned pineapple is processed through a fairly severe heat step, which denatures, or destroys, the enzyme functionality. While the enzyme still technically exists in the canned pineapple, it's no longer able to cut up protein strands.

Don't worry, though—you can still consume the gelatin soup. It makes for a nice drink!

(Note: Instead of canned pineapple, you could make your own protease inactivated pineapple by boiling fresh pineapple. That's actually what I did when developing the experiment, but for sure results, canned is the way to go.)

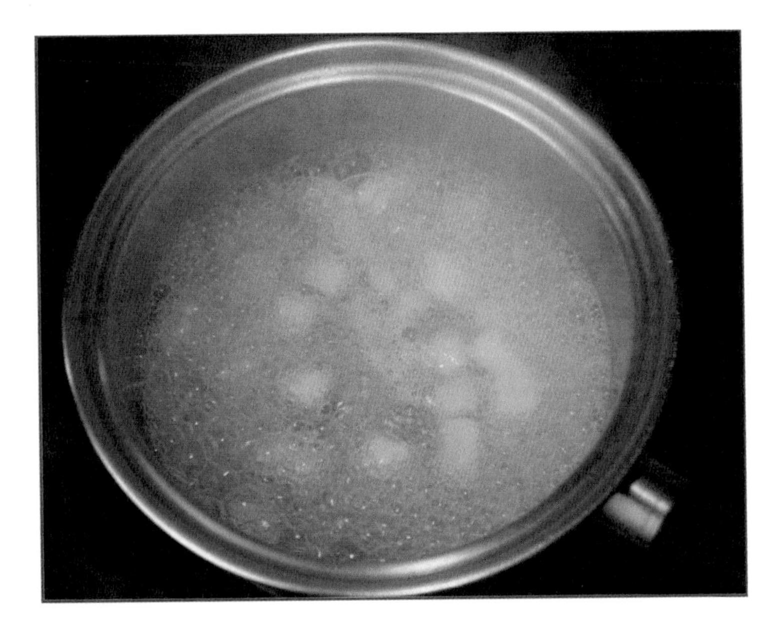

# GENERAL REFERENCES

https://www.engineersedge.com/calculators/levers/page_levers_3.htm

https://www.engineeringtoolbox.com/levers-d_1304.html

https://www.vcalc.com/wiki/KurtHeckman/Simple+Machine

http://www.dynamicscience.com.au/tester/solutions1/hydraulicus/gears1mechanicalad.htm

St. Andre, Ralph. Simple Machines Made Simple. Teachers Ideas Press, a division of Libraries Unlimited, Inc., Englewood, CO (1993).

Kuhn, Karl F. Basic Physics, A Self Teaching Guide. John Wiley & Sons, Inc. (1996).

Hewitt, Paul G. Conceptual Physics. Pearson Education, Inc. (2009).

Serway, Raymond A. and Jerry S Faughn. College Physics. Raymond A. Serway, Saunders College Publishing (1985).

# GLOSSARY

**Accelerate:** Increasing speed.

**Acceleration Due to Gravity:** The acceleration quantity, usually expressed in meters per second per second, or m/s2.

**Block and Tackle:** Referring to the combination of pulley blocks and associated rope or cable rigging, or tackle.

**Complex Machines:** Two or more simple machines constructed together in one machine. See *Simple Machines.*

**Compound Machines:** See *Complex Machines.*

**Conservation of Energy:** The concept that energy can't be created or destroyed, only moved around or balanced.

**Decelerate:** Reducing speed.

**Driver Gear:** A gear in a system that's supplying the original effort force.

**Dynamic Equilibrium:** A physical system that's moving relative to immediate surroundings, but no acceleration is present except for that of gravity. Example: sitting in a car moving at a constant rate of speed.

**Effort Force:** The force generated to accomplish work in a machine. Example: the pushing on the end of a lever to lift something on the other end is effort force.

**Engineering:** The practical application of science, specifically to designing and/or constructing useful items.

**Equilibrium:** Can be static or dynamic. See *Static Equilibrium* and *Dynamic Equilibrium.*

**First-Class Lever:** A lever in which the fulcrum is between the effort and load force.

**Follower Gear:** A gear in a system that isn't the gear supplying the original effort force, but is used to transfer energy from the driver to either another gear, or to accomplish the work.

**Friction:** Describing the resistance to movement across a surface. For example, ice has less friction than sandpaper.

**Fulcrum:** The pivot point of a lever.

**Gear Ratio:** A ratio of the follower gear to the driver gear, or *Gear ratio* = *follower gear* ÷

*driver gear.*

**G-Force:** A multiple of the acceleration due to gravity. Typically used as a reference when describing the rapid acceleration of objects, such as a car or rocket.

**Hydraulics:** A system of machines that exerts force through fluid transfer of energy.

**Inclined Plane:** A simple machine that includes ramps, screws, and wedges as examples.

**Isaac Newton:** A scientist who was instrumental in developing the laws of physics, including what became known as Newton's laws of motion.

**Kinetic Energy:** Energy released from potential energy in many different forms, such as movement or heat.

**Load Force:** The force exerted by a load on a machine.

**Mass:** The amount of material in an object. Combined with the acceleration, mass results in weight. See *Acceleration Due to Gravity*, as well as *Weight*.

**Mechanical Advantage:** Describes the force multiplication of a simple machine.

**Newton:** a measure of force, defined as when the force that, when exerted on a one kilogram mass results in an acceleration of 1 meter/second2.

**Parbuckle:** A complex machine or practice involving an inclined plane and the wheel and axle.

**Physics Engine:** A software program that uses scientific models to simulate real-life interactions in a digital scenario. Physics engines are used in many applications, from video games to stress analysis in manufactured parts.

**Physics:** A branch of science that studies and explains the properties of matter and energy.

**Potential Energy:** Energy available to accomplish work. For example, water behind a dam, or an object suspended above the ground. Both have potential energy that can be harnessed to accomplish work.

**Pulley:** A simple machine application of the wheel and axle, where the effort force is supplied through a rope or cable around the wheel circumference.

**Pulley Block:** A single structure created by combining two or more pulleys.

**Rigging:** A term commonly used to refer to the cables or ropes used in pulley systems.

**Second-Class Lever:** A lever in which the load force is between the effort force and the fulcrum.

**Simple Machines:** Considered to be the most basic machines, with all others being a mixture, or compound, of simple machines. The wheel and axle, lever, and inclined plane are examples of simple machines.

**Speed:** A directionless measurement of motion. See *Velocity*.

**Static Equilibrium:** A physical system at rest, with no parts moving relative to its immediate surroundings, and the only acceleration is that of gravity. Example: sitting in a stationary car.

**Stoichiometry:** The methodical conversion of units from one form to another using established conversion factors. Doing this carefully and in a stepwise fashion reduces errors.

**Third-Class Lever:** A lever in which the effort force is between the fulcrum and the load force.

**Torque:** Rotational or twisting force, usually apparent when speaking of geared systems.

**Universal Joint:** A machine that combines levers and the wheel and axle principles to change the direction of energy along a relatively longitudinal path.

**Velocity:** A measurement of speed plus direction. See *Speed.*

**Wedge:** A machine made by combining two inclined planes back-to-back; designed to exert large spreading forces.

**Weight:** The combination of mass and acceleration. Example: the weight of a lunar rover on Earth weighs less on the moon than on Earth because the acceleration due to gravity is less on the moon. See *Acceleration Due to Gravity,* in addition to Mass.

**Work:** A measure of force exerted over a distance. *Work = force x distance.*

# HINTS FOR CHAPTER REVIEW QUESTIONS

Most of the questions have more than one answer because they're designed to help you think. If you're stuck, maybe these ideas can get you going.

## Chapter 1

1. Think of an icy road, or an underpowered truck with a really heavy load trying to go up a hill.
2. As you increase acceleration, it takes more force to move the same mass.
3. Think of the bouncing astronauts.
4. Other factors include air density, temperature, crosswinds, and the parachute condition (holes, tears, extent of deployment, etc.). In a true vacuum, such as in outer space, no wind resistance exists, so terminal velocity due to the atmosphere doesn't happen. This can be mimicked on Earth by removing the air from a tube. A feather with a high surface area and a steel ball fall at the same rate in these conditions.

## Chapter 2

1. Lots of online resources can help. Typing "levers and the body" in an internet search engine results in a lot of places to go. But as with anything on the internet, you should be cautious and judicious about which sites you go to. Not all information on the internet is correct, or even appropriate for you to view. Please search safely and cautiously!
2. The white crane has a third-class lever on the main boom. The backhoe has a first-class lever on the backhoe arm (the one to the right of the picture). If you find this concept difficult to visualize, search "backhoe" on the internet and find a video showing one in action.

3. You're on your own on this one. You can do it, though!
4. If you have trouble identifying the type, a search on the internet can help as well. You can even find articles that help you understand better about how to identify the types of levers.
5. On your own again. Use your creativity and your imagination!

## Chapter 3

1. Wheelchair ramps, tow trucks that tip to pull cars onto a flatbed, and sidewalk ramps are a few examples.
2. Use wheels or logs, and/or lubrication, such as grease. These are only a couple of examples.
3. As is commonly said, "Necessity is the mother of invention." People needed to perform a task, and with their intelligence and ingenuity, they figured out a way to make it happen. It's amazing what can be accomplished when you focus and put your thoughts to solving a problem!
4. Yes! Taking many small, incremental rises in height over a longer distance is easier than one large step. Spiral stairs are another example...kind of like a screw!
5. Knives are made to accomplish different tasks, although most of us use them for actions they weren't designed for, like as a screwdriver or a small pry bar. For example, some knives cut cheese effectively, slicing through easily. Other knives adhere to either side of the cut, almost acting like glue. This makes for a rough cut as the cheese is compressed, rather than sliced. In this example, the differences are in the knife wedge angle.

## Chapter 4

1. The cross section looks the same as the cross section under the Force Multiplying section, and is the same as for a doorknob.
2. Bicycles and windmills are two more examples.
3. First-class levers are associated with the winch and the rolling log, both using the wheel and axle principle.
4. This one is pretty much right from the text. The crank handle uses leverage to make it easier to wind rope around a cylinder, for example, lifting or pulling an object.

## Chapter 5

1. You want to go to a higher gear ratio to provide more power to the bicycle pedals.
2. Consider a universal joint.
3. You're on your own on this one.
4. To increase power—a piston area function. While not presented in the text, the video link explains it.
5. Shifting at an incorrect time, or consistently using the wrong gear ratio for the application.

# ENDNOTES, PICTURE, AND ILLUSTRATION ATTRIBUTIONS

**Note: Unless otherwise noted, all pictures were taken by Dale W. Cox.**

1 Unless otherwise noted, all photos and drawings were created by Dale W. Cox © 2019.

2 https://www.lexico.com/en/definition/physics, Accessed 20 October 2019. Copyright 2019, Lexico.com.

3 Cars on a freeway, Shadowlink1014 [Public domain], https://commons.wikimedia.org/wiki/File:Us127_east_lansing.jpg, https://upload.wikimedia.org/wikipedia/commons/b/b8/Us127_east_lansing.jpg.

4 Picture of deer, No machine-readable author provided. Exlibris~commonswiki assumed (based on copyright claims). [CC BY-SA 3.0 (http://creativecommons.org/licenses/by-sa/3.0/)], https://commons.wikimedia.org/wiki/File:Mazama_americana.jpg, https://upload.wikimedia.org/wikipedia/commons/8/85/Mazama_americana.jpg.

5 Autodesk is a registered trademark of Autodesk, Inc. You can visit their website at www.autodesk.com.

6 From Conceptual Physics, Paul G. Hewitt, Pearson Education, Inc. Copyright 2009. Pg. 35.

7 Picture of Isaac Newton, Godfrey Kneller [Public domain], https://commons.wikimedia.org/wiki/File:-Sir_Isaac_Newton_by_Sir_Godfrey_Kneller,_Bt.jpg, https://upload.wikimedia.org/wikipedia/commons/5/50/Sir_Isaac_Newton_by_Sir_Godfrey_Kneller%2C_Bt.jpg. Accessed 26 November 2019.

8 Facts About Spacesuits and Space-

walking, NASA, https://www.nasa.gov/audience/foreducators/spacesuits/facts/index.html, last updated 05 July 2018, NASA Content Administrator, NASA Official: Brian Dunbar. Accessed 12 July 2019.

9 Ferrari, Axion23 [CC BY 2.0 (https://creativecommons.org/licenses/by/2.0)], https://commons.wikimedia.org/wiki/File:LaFerrari_in_Beverly_Hills_(14563979888).jpg, https://upload.wikimedia.org/wikipedia/commons/e/e5/LaFerrari_in_Beverly_Hills_%2814563979888%29.jpg. Accessed 13 July 2019.

10 Toyota Corolla, RL GNZLZ from Chile [CC BY-SA 2.0 (https://creativecommons.org/licenses/by-sa/2.0)], https://commons.wikimedia.org/wiki/File:Toyota_Corolla_1.8_LE_2015_(36486832186).jpg, https://upload.wikimedia.org/wikipedia/commons/8/84/Toyota_Corolla_1.8_LE_2015_%2836486832186%29.jpg. Accessed 13 July 2019.

11 Unless otherwise noted, all charts have been created by Dale W. Cox.

12 Bomber sighting equipment, Devon S A (Flt Lt), Royal Air Force official photographer [Public domain], https://commons.wikimedia.org/wiki/File:Royal_Air_Force_Bomber_Command,_1942-1945._CH12283.jpg. Accessed 13 July 2019.

13 Potential energy in a bow, Pierre-Yves Beaudouin / Wikimedia Commons, https://commons.wikimedia.org/wiki/File:2013_FITA_Archery_World_Cup_-_Women%27s_individual_compound_-_Final_-_20.jpg, https://upload.wikimedia.org/wikipedia/commons/1/1a/2013_FITA_Archery_World_Cup_-_Women%27s_individual_compound_-_Final_-_20.jpg. Used under the ***

14 Cox family oak tree, picture taken by LeAnne Cox.

15 Nuclear blast, United States Department of Energy [Public domain], https://commons.wikimedia.org/wiki/File:Castle_Bravo_Blast.jpg, https://upload.wikimedia.org/wikipedia/commons/5/5d/Castle_Bravo_Blast.jpg. Accessed 15 July 2019.

16 Picture of dynamite, FBI [Public domain], https://commons.wikimedia.org/wiki/File:Eric_Rudolph_dynamite.jpg, https://upload.wikimedia.org/wikipedia/commons/3/37/Eric_Rudolph_dynamite.jpg. Accessed 26 November 2019.

17 Paper cutter, Nathan nfm at the English Wikipedia [CC BY-SA 3.0 (http://creativecommons.org/licenses/by-sa/3.0/)], https://commons.wikimedia.org/wiki/File:Paper_cutter_1.jpg, https://upload.wikimedia.org/wikipedia/commons/a/a7/Paper_cutter_1.jpg. Accessed 15 July 2019.

18 Nutcracker, Baran Ivo [Public domain], https://commons.wikimedia.org/wiki/File:Klieste_na_orechy.jpg, https://upload.wikimedia.org/wikipedia/commons/a/a2/Klieste_na_orechy.jpg. Accessed 15 July 2019.

19 Awesome Earthmovers, Screenshot from video. https://www.youtube.com/watch?v=vL-NayfMsNoI.

20 Tweezers, Swathysuren [CC BY-SA 4.0 (https://creativecommons.org/licenses/by-sa/4.0)], https://commons.wikimedia.org/wiki/File:Tweezer.jpg, https://upload.wikimedia.org/wikipedia/commons/e/ed/Tweezer.jpg. Accessed 17 July 2019.

21 Backhoe loader and crane, Andreas PESCH [CC BY-SA 2.0 (https://creativecommons.org/licenses/by-sa/2.0)], https://commons.wikimedia.org/wiki/File:Fermec_backhoe_loader.jpg, https://upload.wikimedia.org/wikipedia/commons/d/d6/Fermec_backhoe_loader.jpg.

Accessed 17 July 2019.

22 The Great Mosque of Samarra. Izzedine [CC BY 3.0 (https://creativecommons.org/licenses/by/3.0)], https://commons.wikimedia.org/wiki/File:Great_Mosque_of_Samarra.jpg, https://upload.wikimedia.org/wikipedia/commons/4/4d/Great_Mosque_of_Samarra.jpg. Accessed 5 July 2019.

23 Pyramids, Slaviboy [CC BY-SA 4.0 (https://creativecommons.org/licenses/by-sa/4.0)], https://commons.wikimedia.org/wiki/File:Naklonena_ravnina_1.PNG, https://upload.wikimedia.org/wikipedia/commons/9/94/Naklonena_ravnina_1.PNG. Accessed 5 July 2019.

24 Horsepower on an inclined plane. Public Domain, https://commons.wikimedia.org/wiki/File:Power_required_on_different_grades.jpg, https://upload.wikimedia.org/wikipedia/commons/7/7f/Power_required_on_different_grades.jpg, Seattle Engineering Department [Public domain]. Accessed 5 July 2019.

25 Moving a barrel up a ramp. Public Domain, https://commons.wikimedia.org/wiki/File:-Chambers_1908_Parbuckle.png, https://upload.wikimedia.org/wikipedia/commons/8/86/Chambers_1908_Parbuckle.png, Rev. Thomas Davidson 1856-1923 (ed.) [Public domain]. Accessed 5 July 2019.

26 Water wheel picture, Photograph by Mike Peel (www.mikepeel.net). [CC BY-SA 4.0 (https://creativecommons.org/licenses/by-sa/4.0)], https://commons.wikimedia.org/wiki/File:Cromford_-_water_wheel_1.jpg, https://upload.wikimedia.org/wikipedia/commons/b/b6/Cromford_-_water_wheel_1.jpg.

27 Gears, ChristianSW [CC BY-SA 3.0 (https://creativecommons.org/licenses/by-sa/3.0)], https://commons.wikimedia.org/wiki/File:Getriebe_Klosterm%C3%BChle_Walsrode.jpg, https://upload.wikimedia.org/wikipedia/commons/5/59/Getriebe_Klosterm%C3%BChle_Walsrode.jpg. Accessed 15 July 2019.

28 Automobile transmission, Herranderssvensson [CC BY-SA 3.0 (https://creativecommons.org/licenses/by-sa/3.0)], https://commons.wikimedia.org/wiki/File:Volvo_M41.jpg, https://upload.wikimedia.org/wikipedia/commons/0/0c/Volvo_M41.jpg. Accessed 15 July 2019.

29 Endless Screw illustration, Rev. Thomas Davidson 1856-1923 (ed.) [Public domain], https://commons.wikimedia.org/wiki/File:-Chambers_1908_Endless_Screw.png, https://upload.wikimedia.org/wikipedia/commons/a/aa/Chambers_1908_Endless_Screw.png. Accessed 13 August 2019.

30 Rack and pinion picture, Rice, Harvey S. [Public domain], https://commons.wikimedia.org/wiki/File:DETAIL_VIEW_OF_RACK_SECTION_AND_DRIVE_PINION_HOISTING_ASSEMBLY_EXTENDING_THROUGH_THE_WEST_WALL_OF_OPERATING_HOUSE_NO._2_FOR_CONTROL_GATE_NO._4,_LOOKING_EAST_-_Long_Lake_HAER_WASH,33-FORD.V,4-A-7.tif, https://upload.wikimedia.org/wikipedia/commons/3/3d/DETAIL_VIEW_OF_RACK_SECTION_AND_DRIVE_PINION_HOISTING_ASSEMBLY_EXTENDING_THROUGH_THE_WEST_WALL_OF_OPERATING_HOUSE_NO._2_FOR_CONTROL_GATE_NO._4%2C_LOOKING_EAST_-_Long_Lake_HAER_WASH%2C33-FORD.V%2C4-A-7.tif.jk. Accessed 13 August 2019.

Made in the USA
Middletown, DE
24 January 2023